BRINGING BIRTH HOME

INSPIRATION FOR BIRTH BEYOND THE HOSPITAL

COLLEEN REAGAN   KATIE ROSE   KARYN BESLEY

LUCIA STUART   CORINNE BROWN

ALISON SEDLAK

DR. AMANDA CLEARY PICKART, PT, DPT

PAULA FADWAH HALEY   YAEL JULANOV

ANNE HANCOCK   BARBARA HARPER

ALIA WRIGHT   BETHANY A. LECLERC

KYLEIGH BANKS   MAIA WENTRUP

ASHLEY AUGUSTINE

WISE WOMEN BOOK COLLECTIVE

CONTENTS

DISCLAIMER

The publisher and the authors are providing this book and its contents on an "as is" basis and make no representations or warranties of any kind with respect to this book or its contents. The publisher and the authors disclaim all such representations and warranties, including but not limited to warranties of healthcare for a particular purpose. In addition, the publisher and the authors assume no responsibility for errors, inaccuracies, omissions, or any other inconsistencies herein.

The content of this book is for informational purposes only and is not intended to diagnose, treat, cure, or prevent any condition or disease. You understand that this book is not intended as a substitute for consultation with a licensed practitioner. Please consult with your own physician or healthcare specialist regarding the suggestions and recommendations made in this book. The use of this book implies your acceptance of this disclaimer.

INTRODUCTION

When a friend found out I was organizing a book on home birth after hospital birth and that I am planning a home birth for whenever I have another child, her response was, "That's surprising after how your first birth turned out that you would want to!" My first birth was an emergency cesarean that I do believe was an emergency. In fact, I think that my late pregnancy/birth should have had more medical intervention than it had. Even with that, and partly because of that, I have been drawn in to learn more about home birth.

The first time I found out that I was pregnant, I was living in downtown Boston. I was thinking about a local birth center or a home birth. The proximity to so many major hospitals made home birth seem less scary for me, and I didn't like the hospital where the birth center patients were transferred to if needed. Unfortunately, that pregnancy ended in a miscarriage, as did the next one. By the time I was pregnant with my first child, we had moved out of the city. The experience of the two miscarriages greatly affected me, and I was no longer as confident in the entire pregnancy process as I had been previously. I was happy to find that the local hospital had a midwife group and signed on for care with them. The pregnancy was not an easy one as I threw up every day until I was 36 weeks along, and I was monitored for growth restriction in the baby from twenty-five weeks on. Despite all of that, the hardest part of the pregnancy was the care I received from the midwives. I have always been a birth junkie. I had taken a doula training course and went through the HypnoBirthing instructor training before having kids, so I thought I knew how birth was supposed to go and that midwives would be the best choice. What I did not realize was the large discrepancy between a hospital midwife group and a home birth midwife. They are two entirely different experiences.

The midwife group was comprised of quite a few midwives, some OBs, and a few nurse practitioners. Every appointment was with a new person, and I would have to start from the beginning of why I hadn't gained much weight (the vomiting) and that I had been sent to maternal-fetal medicine many times for the possible growth restriction, with a baby measuring 1% off from where he would be considered growth restricted. I was never met in an appointment with friendliness. I never felt like I established any connection with anyone. I would come home from each appointment a wreck. The only person who was a consistent, friendly face for that pregnancy was the scheduler at the ultrasound office at the hospital; she remembered me more than any of the midwives. Any concern I wanted to ask about, I would call the main number, a nurse would take a message, and after consulting the doctor, a nurse would call me back with the answer. There were no personal touches at all.

As my pregnancy closed in on its last few weeks, my baby still measured small. I remember at 38 weeks, I was sent for a biophysical profile. While in there, the baby was not responsive in the ways he should have been. I remember the ultrasound tech telling me that I would probably be induced that day based on what he saw. He gave it a last few minutes, and finally, my baby had some sort of response. It was considered a passed test, and all that was conveyed to the midwife practice was that he passed. A few days later, the same thing happened with a non-stress test. I had no point of contact to talk to in the practice. No one seemed to be getting any notes other than the baby had eventually passed the biophysical profile and the non-stress test. My 39 week appointment was with one of the OBs of the practice. The first time I had seen an OB during my pregnancy instead of a midwife or nurse practitioner. I was very concerned at this point with the small size of my baby and the two nearly failed tests and expressed my concern to him. He responded that I should make sure I'm doing my kick counts as a baby measuring as small as mine was at risk for stillbirth. Then he left the room. I went another week before I went into labor. The baby didn't tolerate labor, and his birth was an emergency cesarean. When he was born, they discovered a very short, skinny umbilical cord, and he was much smaller than they had anticipated being, and they had anticipated him being small. He didn't have an ounce of fat on him—just skin and bones.

I often think about how that pregnancy would have gone differently had I had a more caring provider or a main provider instead of the disjointed care. I do believe that birth would have ended up in hospital care even had I planned a home birth, but I think about how the care would have been handled up to that point and how much more comforting it would have been, and how much more knowledge I could have received.

With my second child, I knew I wanted a VBAC. After how my first pregnancy had gone, I felt like the hospital was the right place to try for my VBAC—a decision based mostly on fear. I switched away from the midwife practice as fast as I could, and I had a much better experience with the all OB practice. It was still a large practice with very disjointed care, but as this pregnancy was much easier and there were no issues, it didn't seem to be a problem. I was lucky and met very little resistance to having a VBAC, and I went into labor on my own on my due date. I had two days of early labor before things started to really pick up. With my first labor, I had some back and forth from the hospital that I hated, and I was very focused on this labor getting to where it was that I was going to be when I gave birth and settling in for the long haul. With no room at the inn, the hospital sent me back home, and my husband filled up the jacuzzi tub.

It was on that tub that the franticness and despair that accompanied the first part of that day disappeared. I was able to relax and work with the contractions instead of against them. My 22 month old son was able to join me in the tub to nurse before he went down for his nap, my husband was able to relax and do his thing around the house, and I lost all track of time until my water broke and I entered transition.

Cue the frantic energy again. I got in the car with no shoes on, held onto the bar on the roof by the window in the car, and squatted while pushing the whole drive to the hospital. Thank goodness we didn't get into an accident! There were still no rooms available when we arrived, and I was told to stop pushing and hold my baby in until they could get a doctor. This is very hard to do when the natural expulsion reflex kicks in, and it felt like quite a long time before the doctor showed up, and they were able to bring all of the equipment into the triage room. When I was finally allowed to push, it was coached pushing. My baby was out in two contractions, but I could feel myself pushing too hard, and I lived with the effects of that for weeks after the birth. I was having a normal and natural birth until the car ride, hospital, and doctor interfered. What could have been a beautiful home birth was instead a medically managed birth, even without the use of any drugs or medications.

I have spent a lot of time thinking over my two birth experiences and keep coming to the same thoughts. One being that low-risk births probably come with less risks and side effects when done at home.

Another is that I am very thankful to live in a time period in which births that need medical intervention have resources and that there are medical professionals who are very skilled at births with complications. The last is that being thrown around from one provider to another for the entire pregnancy and not meeting who will deliver my baby until two weeks before my due date, or in the case of my first while I was being wheeled into surgery, is not the way to feel supported and confident in a pregnancy. I had a total of 21 different providers over two pregnancies.

Home birth, which had been pushed to the back of my mind since the second miscarriage, started resurfacing as a thought in my head. When the Covid-19 pandemic hit, I started to hear of more women choosing home birth. It was on the heels of a book I produced in late 2020, "Baby Got VBAC", that birthed this thought of looking into home birth further and in a unique way. I know there are others like me out there that don't feel like the way they had their previous births was going to work for them anymore. With reasons ranging from trauma and Covid to feeling like they are being called home, everyone leaning in this direction has a unique path that brings them here.

I am so amazed at the women who have stepped forward to share their journeys to having a home birth after a hospital birth and the wisdom they provide purely from sharing their stories. In addition, the midwives in this book offer their experience and expertise.

My hope is that reading this book will help guide you to follow your intuition, no matter which path that leads you down. Each author is speaking from their own personal experience, and they are only representing themselves in their chapter. The beauty of a book like this is to see people from different viewpoints and walks of life be able to share their truth and what was right for them and their family.

Many of our authors have shared their social media handles and contact info. Please feel free to follow them or reach out if their chapter has particularly resonated with you.

Colleen Reagan Noon, Founder of the Wise Women Book Collective

Stories From

Australia

1

HOMEBIRTH AFTER HOSPITAL

KATIE ROSE

'The first thing that you do when you come into this life is to inhale. The last thing you will do when you leave this life is to exhale. What happens in-between is the journey of your lifetime.' Sharon Gannon (founder Jivamukti Yoga)

Empowerment

IN OUR CURRENT culture and time in history, we are generally not nurtured to trust our intuition or to exercise our autonomy (even with our own bodies). We are institutionalised from a very young age and taught to conform, to bend to authority, and to trust those who 'know more than us.' Sometimes this is necessary, but in the birthing space, these years of conditioning often leave women feeling powerless and fearing they will be unable to birth their babies. We don't trust our bodies. We don't trust our wild-selves (and birthing is perhaps the most primal we'll ever be). A natural birth cannot be stripped of its animal nature. It should not be. But our birthing culture has been sanitised and medicalised.

How do we re-wild ourselves? This is perhaps the most potent tool in preparing for birthing a baby. Re-wilding, re-membering (drawing all the lost parts of ourselves back together), and cultivating an awe for our animal capacity, not a revulsion of it.

Some of the ways that have worked for me have been enjoying sex and learning not to be too self-conscious in that space. Being able to look into her partner's eyes during love-making or allow her partner to look after her when she is vulnerable (for example, vomiting or unwell) sets a woman up for the beautiful vulnerability of birthing her baby. Sanitising the sexual act or feeling very self-conscious about your body or making a sound or being looked at during love-making are often precursors to a sanitised, medicalised birth. We are not at ease with our bodies and what they do in their wild state.

Spending time in nature has also supported my re-wilding. Jumping into the ocean, walking barefoot in the grass, sleeping under the stars.

I have heard women talk about the 'orgasmic birthing' experience and always thought that sounded crazy! I couldn't imagine it—my experiences of birthing four babies and supporting many more women to birth theirs is that it is painful and arduous. But there is an ecstasy in there, too, and a wildness that mirrors the moment of orgasm. Perhaps the idea isn't as crazy as I first thought.

Hospitals are not generally great environments for empowered choices. They are not places where the wild in us flourishes. The Russian women who 'sea birth' know this. Aboriginal Australian women who birth 'On Country' in birthing caves or by birth trees know this. Women who choose to homebirth know this.

When, as women, we consciously and deliberately set the intention and do the practices to awaken and connect to our intuitive capacity (another way of thinking about 're-wilding'), we set ourselves up for a positive birthing experience. To go back to the link with our sexual experiences—if you can figure out what you like and don't like, ask for what you want and say no to what you don't want, you're in for a much better experience. It is the same in birthing. We speak so much about the need for consent in the post #metoo era. What about empowerment and consent in the world of birthing our babies?

As a doula, the number of times women have said to me, 'I didn't know I could choose that' is astounding. Our Western medical system is set up for handing over power, a paradigm most of us have been subjugated to from as young as we remember. What is the difference between a birth a woman can feel empowered about and one she does not? It is not the outcome. The difference is autonomy; feeling like you made choices about what happened to your body and your baby.

A woman may go into the hospital wishing for a natural birth and end up having a c-section and feel okay about that if she feels like she (and her partner) were actively engaged and involved in the decisions that lead to the intervention. On the other hand, a natural vaginal birth may happen, but if the birthing woman doesn't feel safe or respected during the process, it's not an empowering experience.

In some ways, the environment isn't important. But we can ask which conditions are most likely to lead to an empowered outcome. For many women, because of the power dynamics and institutionalised paradigm of disregarding a woman's own knowing and intuitive sense of her body present in the hospital setting, the most empowering place to birth will be at home.

Finding Ease in the Unknown

'It takes the same amount of energy to carry your trauma as it does to carry your destiny. But you can't carry both. You will have to choose.'
Guru Jagat

I am a yoga teacher, and I have studied the Sanskrit scriptures over many years. There is a beautiful Sanskrit word that is difficult to translate into English. The word is 'swaha'. It can loosely be translated as 'Let Go and Let God'. God being interpreted in the broadest sense in this context—whatever it is that lights you up and brings you beyond your small self. God as the sunrise over the ocean, God as the majestic oak tree, God when you gaze into the eyes of your newborn baby. Swaha points to a way of being in the world that says, I'll do my best, I'll give it my all, and then I'll surrender.

A good example of when this might apply is a job interview for a position you really want. You prepare your resume. You go to bed early the night before. You wear the right clothing and do some research about the company you wish to work for. You take the interview, and the rest is out of your hands. Maybe the job is yours, and maybe another better candidate comes along. Maybe you are meant not to get the job because the richest lessons and highest good is not there for you in that job you think you want so much.

Childbirth is the ultimate test of our ability to 'swaha'. It doesn't matter where you birth or with whom the outcome is not in your hands. I've already mentioned our cultural bias towards devaluing intuition. We also have a cultural bias towards being in control. Our whole society is built on controlling the world outside of us. On a macro level, we control the environment, the animals, and each other. On a micro-level, we control the temperature of the house we live in and the algorithm of the information we digest. Birthing our babies is one of the few areas where control is still limited. Perhaps that's why it's so confronting to so many women. We're just not used to not being in control. Now my children are growing; I also see that this is analogous with parenting. I can't control what my children do as they become adults. All I can do is hope I've set good conditions for them to make good choices and then 'swaha'—let go.

When we make the choice to homebirth—especially when we make that choice after having had a very 'controlled' hospital birth—we make a choice for freedom and letting go. This doesn't mean taking medical risks or being irresponsible. It does mean working on our own capacity to step into unknowns and being brave enough to sit comfortably with whatever comes up. At the time of writing, we are just over a year into the global Corona Virus pandemic. This last year has taught us all a great deal about sitting in the unknown. Some of us have contracted and tightened up, unable to handle the new reality, which isn't predictable, and may not feel safe. In the same way with birthing, some women choose the 'safety' of a hospital because they feel like it makes birthing a more predictable event. Maybe it does, but what is lost in that predictable container? What's the cost of control over freedom? Others of us have extended ourselves into embracing not-knowing and, by default, then arrived in a place of embracing the present moment more deeply. In my own life, I have found this is what it takes to birth a baby with empowerment and raise a child with grace.

Simple Rituals are Powerful

My own home birthing experience was with my second child. He was born during an outrageously vigorous thunderstorm on the deck of our home in a birthing pool. He's a wild child, and he was born in on a wild night! His birth was special because of the magical way in which my midwife held sacred space for me. It felt like my midwife 'did' very little but also 'did' everything by holding the powerful presence of possibility. She believed in my capacity. She believes in her own skill and experience. The ritualistic element of primal birthing was possible in that container.

Path of Effort Path of Grace

Another great yogic principle is the paradox of the 'Path of Effort' and the 'Path of Grace'. The path of effort (known as Maryada Marga in Sanskirt) is also sometimes called the lawful way. In yoga tradition, this is where the practitioner's own discipline and self-effort bring her to the goal. On this path, we follow particular guidelines and rules for a predictable outcome. For example, if I want a more flexible and healthy body, I get on my yoga mat and do some postures every day. In the world of birthing, this is not the most useful pathway to take. Of course, birthing a baby takes effort! But the skill is in the surrender. The Path of Grace (known as Pushti Marga in Sanskrit) happens when the practitioner lets go and allows the energy of Source to move through her. Call it by any name you like: God, Krishna, Allah, Jehovah ... this power is what conceives, births, and ultimately transitions our lives at the end. Surrender to this Path of Grace is what I have learned through birthing four babies and particularly on the thunderous night at home with my second boy.

Both the path of effort and the path of grace can only bring the practitioner to the doorway of liberation - it is the energy of the Divine that ultimately and gracefully carries us across the threshold.

Another way of thinking about effort and grace is control and surrender. In the world of birthing, the best application of control is in being counter-culture enough in the hospital environment to staunchly hold space for a woman to birth in grace—to be left alone.

Feminine Form Healthcare Practice

For far too long, our healthcare institutions, hospitals, and surgeries have been dominated by the patriarchy. Feminine form holistic healthcare practice is less of a hierarchy and more of a collaboration. The best doulas and midwives do very little. They hold space, they weave magic, and they set an intention. They don't feel the need to 'look busy' or bustle. They've mastered the art of being and not doing.

Let me give you an example of feminine form practice compared to mainstream hospital-based practice. I am a trained doula, and I've been practicing as a childbirth support person for many years. As a doula, I meet with my new 'clients'—the women whom I will support on the pathway of birthing their babies—several times before the 'birthday'. It is usual for doulas to ask many questions of their clients at this time to find out about their birth hopes and dreams, and history. The usual set of questions can be quite prescriptive, feeling somewhat like a medical questionnaire. One of my mentors made a suggestion to me years ago that was very powerful. She said, how about we throw that questionnaire out the window and start by asking our clients, 'What do you know about how your Grandmother birthed your mother?'.

Over the years, I've now asked that question to many, many women, and the answers are always profoundly moving and rich in their capacity to open us up to deeper and more sincere dialogue. We must get over our social niceties and candy-coated 'tick-box' mentality if we are to stand any chance of re-wilding our birthing experiences. We must ask the harder questions of ourselves and each other. Dive a little deeper. Poke around in the murky bits and curiously wonder about our grandmothers, and their grandmothers and the gold chain of women before us.

Birthing on Country – a story of Indigenous 'Homebirthing'

I live on the East Coast of Australia, close to a river location named Dangar Island, where Aboriginal birthing caves have been located for thousands of years. These days the caves are not used, but I have visited them many times, sometimes when pregnant with my own babes, and felt the deep power of their history. A cave itself is a portal and also reminiscent of the birthing canal through which the baby will arrive earthside.

The caves were a birthing place for the women of the Guringai Nation and a ritual site for women and infants only. The rocks are inscribed with marks that we can no longer make sense of. Were they tribal records? Records of the babies born, lost, and mourned ... a tracking of the family lineages? We may never know, but there is something special about a place for women and babies only, where safe birthing can occur close to the ocean. There are many small rock pools, and I have often imagined women over hundreds of years using them as a birthing pool. I personally do not advocate 'free-birth' and believe it is very important to have a qualified midwife, with medical equipment if needed, present for the birth of a baby. But I dream of a time where we can meet in the middle and embrace our ancestral roots and those of the land we live on whilst honouring the need for medical intervention when it arises.

In 2019 my friend Renee Adair who founded the Australian Doula College, partnered with Charles Darwin University to co-facilitate an Accredited Doula training for Indigenous women in the remote First Nations community of Galiwin'ku. The project brought together ancient knowing with contemporary learning methodologies and pioneered a reawakening of First Nations wisdom where it might have been lost. The land helps us to remember when we watch it.

Many Aboriginal women in Australia, especially those in more remote regions, prefer to birth their babies 'on Country' (on the land of their ancestral lineage). This means the baby is born within the ancestral 'lines' of his or her lineage and is important within Indigenous Australian culture. This birthing 'On Country' is not always possible because there may not be adequate sanitation or health care facilities. But the Charles Darwin University project has found a way to bring the worlds together. While many women do have to birth 'off Country', they are supported by 'one of their own', a doula who knows their language and offers consistency of care and a remembering of culture.

Universal Remembering

It is important not to glorify the 'good old days' when many more women and babies died in childbirth. We have much to be grateful for in modern medicine. However, before we get on our knees and bow down to the Holy Shrine of Obstetrics, we might also do well to remember where we've come from. We might do well to remember our animal nature and our instinctive drive to collaborate. As a species, we are hard-wired to care for each other and to care for the more vulnerable members of our communities. TV shows like 'Call the Midwife' and books like those of the legendary Ina May Gaskin appeal to us because they highlight birth stories that take place in a context. There is a feeling of community and story. This is a key ingredient in a positive birthing experience and far more likely to happen in a homebirth where you will know your midwife than in a hospital where you may be seen by several doctors or midwives whom you've never met before. These are the universal principles of a positive birthing experience beyond cultural context or details.

One of my favourite herbalists and lay medicine teachers, Mila Prince, says on sharing healing culture, '*We share and tend to our community near and far both as a business and through mutual aid.*' This sentiment to resonant for me. There is an energy of 'tending', caring for, and slowly nurturing. Again, this echoes the journey of motherhood. We look out for those who need extra care. It's not all about money or 'outcomes'. There is a focus on being skilfully responsive in the moment.

We only need to look at a practice as simple and perfect as Yoni Steaming to see how women's wisdom is beyond cultural context and appropriation. Yoni Steaming has been embodied by women from literally all over the globe as a traditional method of care, hygiene, healing, embodiment, and reverence for our sexuality. Yoni Steaming represents to me the meeting place of ritual and practical application. As a practice, it serves both to cleanse in the metaphorical sense and in the literal sense. In his ground-breaking book, 'Voices of the First Day', Robert Lawlor writes of smoking the yoni in Aboriginal culture at the beginning of labour. He describes, '*The midwife's actions are both practical and symbolic. Smoking the baby with herbs and exposing it to ash have both hygienic value and significance for ritual purification.'*

The methods and the process vary, but the sentiment is the same. We can often, usually, heal ourselves in our kitchens, in our communities, with information passed down from our ancestors and lay-support people. We can start here at least and venture into mainstream health care if and when it is really needed.

If we are intelligent in our approach, we will lean into the most healed and luminous birthing practices from all cultures and from all times in history (including the modern day). We will tread the universal pathways of sanctity, choice, and our wild, wild selves with respect and reverence.

REFERENCES:

Russian women 'sea birthing' https://newageru.hypotheses.org/5204

Guru Jagat https://ramayogainstitute.com

Sharon Gannon www.jivamuktiyoga.com

Milla Prince https://www.instagram.com/p/CNSim7nsxej/

'Voices of the First Day' author Robert Lawlor

Renee Adair and Charles Darwin University project https://www.australiandoulacollege.com.au/galuwinku

KATIE ROSE

Katie Rose is an inspirational teacher bringing yoga, ayurveda and mindfulness to busy modern-day women. Her impressive wealth of knowledge, along with her solid spiritual grounding and no-nonsense approach has earnt her an enthusiastic following of women from all walks of life.

A published author of several books and founder of many successful yoga businesses, Katie is passionate about empowering women to live a healthy, happy and balanced life. She covers a broad range of wellness and self-care practices, but more importantly helps her students reconnect to a sense of devotion and sacredness in everyday life.

Her teachings draw on her background as an advanced level Jivamukti Yoga and Kundalini Yoga teacher, her work as an ayurvedic consultant and birth-work as a practicing doula. A mother of four boys, Katie diligently attempts to practice what she teaches; focusing on a happy, healthy family life.

Website: www.BhaktiRose.com.au

2

PRIVATELY PRACTICING ENDORSED MIDWIFE

NEW SOUTH WALES, AUSTRALIA

KARYN BESLEY

I REMEMBER my first day as a student midwife; I sat amongst a small group of women, equally excited to start their journey; when asked what our 10-year vision was, I proudly stated I would be running my own homebirth practice. Ironic, as I was sitting in the tearoom of a large private hospital maternity unit: the most highly medicalised birth model in Australia. I knew I would get there; it would be a long road ......15 years later, I proudly opened the doors to Hunter Homebirth.

At the time I studied midwifery (1997), I only had one option, a post-graduate diploma of midwifery: an extra year after a 3-year Bachelor of Nursing. The small portion of birth I witnessed during my nursing was far from appealing; I witnessed a culture of fear and danger and intervention: far from what I heartfelt knew birth to be.

I had grown up in an era of new freedoms. My mother was the arche-type 1970's free love feminist. My sister and I grew up surrounded by powerful women, where birth and breastfeeding were the norm. I knew that women were created to birth and that the patriarchal system did not support this. My first memory of birth was a friend of my mum's (a single 40 year old woman: far from common in 1980) in early labour in our lounge, she had come into town to be closer to her birth centre; I can remember feeling initially scared; but being 100% reassured as mum, and the other women loved and cared for Marg as she progressed in her early labour. I remember being shown her birth photos a few days later: feeling in awe of what this amazing woman had achieved. From this experience grew my interest in how I might birth my own babies in the future.

Midwifery wasn't initially my calling. As I said, I had witnessed horrendous care during my student nurse days. It was my own births that made me realise I could be a part of ensuring women's experiences were positive. I loved my midwives, and I knew that was what I would do. I loved the experience of being with women. I felt naturally drawn to pregnant women or those with young babies and children. I was in the same life stage as them, so words came easily, and I was able to relate to the women in my care. I quickly found my niche in midwifery. I was employed in a team model of care, a small group of midwives working shifts in a roster designed to ensure the women met all the midwives antenatally so that in birth, she would have that familiar face and known carer. The idea of a team program was that all midwives shared a similar philosophy so that women knew their preferences would be upheld regardless of which midwife was on shift. This program also allowed us to do home visits after the birth. Postnatal visits were in the home, allowing new mums to stay at home and still receive support and education.

Although this model was said to be the 'gold standard 'of midwifery-led care in Australia at that time, I felt it lacked the benefits of home. The shift work meant I was missing many of the births of my own clients because I was rostered off or had worked over my hours by helping out others who were on days off. I found it upsetting to have to send my clients to a doctor review if they declined normal care. I wanted to have full autonomy, to be able to see women in their own homes on their terms. I wanted to be able to provide full continuity of care by being the primary care provider for the entire pregnancy, birth, and six weeks postpartum. During my employment in hospitals, I had acquired all the skills I needed for independent practice, such as suturing and emergency care competency. I had networked and gained a sense of respect around the local area. I had made connections with other private midwives who were already practicing, providing mentorship, professional support, and the basic day to day running of a business.

My first homebirth client was a couple that I had known for a few years. They had birthed their 2nd daughter with me when I worked at the hospital. They were halfway through their 3rd pregnancy when I made the decision to go private. This couple decided to continue their care with me and have a homebirth—what a dream start I had. Not only did we all know each other well, they lived less than a 10-minute drive from me. One lovely rainy Sunday morning a few months later, she birthed her 3rd daughter into my brand-new birthing pool in her loungeroom. It felt so normal, so amazingly absolutely out of this world, exciting and powerful—yet so normal. Her little girls watched on in awe. Her parents arrived and helped out with the excited older sisters as I tucked mum and new baby up into a nest on her couch, where she would spend the next few days in awe of life. I drove the few minutes home with the utmost joy, knowing I was finally where I had always wanted to be practicing midwifery as it is meant to be, allowing women full control and autonomy, bringing birth home.

During the early days of my practice, I attended homebirths with other PPEMs to gain experience and to watch how each one worked. This provided me with a wealth of experience and the confidence to continue on. Jody was my next client and the first that I had met at six weeks pregnant. Again, she lived within a 10-minute drive from me, but this wasn't to last. I now drive an average of 90minutes to each client. She was having her 3rd homebirth; the first two were in a rural area with a different midwife. So, she became my 'midwife'.

Through her own experience as a home birthing woman, she was able to offer encouragement and ideas on ways to support birth outside of the hospital. I greatly appreciated her words of wisdom, and this further encouraged my passion. Very quickly, I found myself fully booked and loving it.

Again and again, I witness the beautiful unfolding of a true physiological birth, where time does not matter, and routine checks are absent. It is well researched that a woman will birth best in the place she feels safest. She is in her home, her safe place, her comfort zone. She is surrounded by all she loves, people, memories, foods, and sounds. As I enter a home, I am acutely aware that I am the visitor. It is me who needs to ask permission. I was privileged to care for clients who had birthed with me in the hospital. They would choose to homebirth as we already built the midwife/woman relationship.

What could be more amazing, it's the early hours of the morning, I quietly enter a home, tiptoe in and gently place a hand on her head and neck to acknowledge my presence, sit back and observe. The soft walls of the inflatable birth pool allow her to rest deeply between surges. I've been to the home around ten times during the antenatal period, so I know it well. There is no need for her to tell me her story or explain her history because I know her already. Generally, I've seen her within the past few days; therefore, I know the position of her baby, a quick set of observations is enough. It is not necessary to have her sit up on a bed and have a full examination. Thus, protecting her from interruption of her natural processes. She is aware that I will be asking first and quietly having short listens to her baby's heart rate whilst she is in the pool. The beauty of having this relationship allows for all the preparations to be done prior to the birth. The antenatal period is an exquisite time where the relationship between the pregnant woman, her partner, family, and the midwife evolves. I use current evidence to assist in informed decision-making for all aspects of care. Without the overriding fear of hospital policy, I am fully able to support women's choices. I inform clients of the recommended care, provide current research, and plan each decision. The birth is not mine, nor is it my place to make any decisions for the couple.

Another client had a difficult labour and emergency section whilst under my care in the hospital. It was one of those days where every baby decides to come. I was made to leave half-way through her labour because I had already been in the unit for over 12 hours and birthed two babies. I will never know if this impacted her journey, but she was taken for an emergency cesarean later that night. This was very traumatic for her. This was nearing the end of my time working in the system. I never forgave myself for letting her down that day until 18 months later, she called to ask if I would be her homebirth midwife. The next few months, we worked together, and on a New Year Day, she birthed her 2nd son into the pool in her own loungeroom. This birth was as healing for me as much as for her. I finally felt that I could forgive myself for letting her down the first time.

A client had booked me for her 3rd baby. She had a vaginal breech birth four years prior and a cephalic home water-birth two years prior. She was declined access to the local midwifery-led model due to a known anatomic anomaly within her uterus (bicornuate uterus: a joining in the septum causing a heart-shaped appearance). This anomaly meant she was more prone to have babies in the breech position. From booking, she was aware that homebirth could only occur if this baby remained head down at the time of labour. The baby was compliant, and it was looking like we'd be birthing at home until her 36-week appointment. She and I both knew that he had turned. Due to the uterine anomaly, I was unable to offer her referral to an obstetrician to attempt to turn her baby. Thankfully the local public hospital is well known for its support for breech vaginal births, with women coming from all areas to breech birth vaginally, rather than the elective cesarean offered by others. In collaboration with the obstetricians, we had a plan of care to ensure her birth wishes were upheld, and her baby remained safe. I attended her home in early labour, and we all went to the hospital together, where we were met with the utmost respect. She was given full autonomy in all her choices. The obstetric team sat outside the room while I assisted her vaginal breech birth. She stayed for a few hours and then headed home. This was a wonderful example of how well our models of care can work together to ensure the best outcomes for women and babies.

Of course, every now and then, emergencies occur. However, I find that women are less scared by the event than a similar situation in a hospital. The procedures in a hospital involve bright lights, loud bells, multiple staff on emergency response teams which is all very overwhelming. In the home, it's controlled in a quiet way. If a transfer becomes necessary, our ambulance service is fabulous. They come very quickly, and they can assist with life support of mum and/or bub until arrival at the nearest birth unit. I go with them to the hospital and stay on for support as long as needed. Our birth kits are comprehensive, including neonatal resuscitation, oxygen, suction, and equipment for cannulation and catheterisation. As well as medications such as syntocinon, voltaren, antibiotics, and anti-emetics. I am competent in maternity emergency training and attend these skills regularly. I have a second midwife attend births, just at the end, in case of need for emergency care. Legally a second midwife is required at all births.

This client had been with me for her 4th child. Again, I had feelings of guilt after having let her down by being forced to hand her care over to doctors at 42-weeks gestation, and I was on a mandatory day off when she did finally go into labour. She booked me for a home-birth for her 5th child, relaxed in the knowledge that she would have no pressures around going postdates, as all her previous four had. Ironically this baby decided to arrive at around 38 weeks! This little girl arrived in the evening, feet first, surrounded by her four older siblings. I don't attend known breech births at home. This little girl surprised us all. Her birth was so fast. By the time we realised her feet were presenting, the entire baby was out. Upon reflection, Rebecca and her family stated they had no idea there was an 'obstetric emergency 'occurring and were shocked to know she would have had a cesarean if she had presented to the hospital with an undiagnosed breech baby.

In Australia, approximately 8% of women receive midwifery-led continuity of care. For the majority of women, care is received in a fragmented model. This means different care providers are seen at each visit. Whilst this can end in a wonderful birth experience, it is dependent on the ability of both the woman and the midwife being able to create a rapport and trust in a very short time, and sometimes within the throws of labour. Women speak of the pain in having to constantly repeat their history to each new care provider, which is especially upsetting when there is a history of trauma or abuse.

The midwifery curriculum in Australia aims to have midwives competent in working across the full scope of practice, ideally working within a continuity of care model (caseload, every woman has a known midwife). Midwives are trained to work within our professional guidelines, where women are at the centre. This is counterintuitive when we begin to work in the hospital setting. Currently, midwives must work in the system for five years full-time (or equivalent) to be eligible to apply for the endorsement process to step into private practice.

In Australia, most births are attended in hospitals. There is still a strong culture towards the risk-based approach; babies should be born in hospital 'just in case "; despite current research stating homebirth is as safe, if not safer, for low-risk women.

In a hospital, midwives are employed by the institution and, as such, are expected to work within the hospital policies and guidelines. Midwives are not encouraged to support women to choose care outside the guidelines. Midwives support women to achieve the birth they wish for, as long as this is within the recommended guidelines.

Whilst many women are content to go along with this care, accepting it as 'best practice', many are not. The role of the midwife is directly subordinate to the medical colleagues, thus beginning the power struggle and fight for her client's wishes. During training, it was drummed in that I was professionally covered for complaint or damage only IF I stayed within hospital policy.

When a newly pregnant woman presents to her general practitioner, she will be asked if she has private health insurance. If yes, the referral will be given to a private hospital. If no, she will be given a referral to the local public hospital. This is the start of a pregnancy journey for women unless they have been educated and made aware of the true options. I sometimes get calls from amazingly motivated women, not yet pregnant, researching the options available to them. They are called "TTC" trying to conceive. I find women become disillusioned over the course of the pregnancy, sometimes at 20 weeks, sometimes as late as 38 weeks. Social media platforms encourage women to investigate their options and question things. I have women call me saying they had seen women with the same story online, and they want to discuss the option of homebirth. Ideally, I meet women and their families at the beginning of a pregnancy. This allows us to create the relationship which forms the base to the unfolding physiological process of birth. I see the relief on women's faces when they find an alternative to the model in which they want to leave. Women now question any investigation, screening test, or medication. It is a basic human right to be given correct and unbiased information in a non-coercive manner. Information sheets or pamphlets need to show all the options, risks, and reasons, including the option of not attending it.

A client contacted me when she was 34 weeks pregnant with her 4th child. She had initially booked at her local public hospital with the understanding that she would be supported to have a VBAC2CS (vaginal birth after cesarean, history of two previous cesareans). Emily had previously had two cesareans. A VBAC for one previous cesarean is commonplace in Australia. However, greater than one previous cesarean is not yet supported in most hospitals despite research showing a very small difference between one or two previous cesarean births. *QUOTE*. She had seen multiple carers during her visits and was under the impression that she would be supported to VBAC2CS. At her 34-week appointment with the obstetrician, she was told she would not be able to attempt VBAC and would be made to have a cesarean. We met that day. I found Emily to be extremely well informed. Her last cesarean birth was seven years prior, and she had a strong belief that her body could do this. She was also prepared to transfer to the hospital if any complications arose. We created a plan together based on my risk assessment. This covered things like the need for spontaneous labour and regular monitoring of her baby's heart rate. She went into labour at 37 weeks. It was winter, and the birth pool was placed in front of the open fire. She birthed her baby girl into her own hands, alongside her husband and three sons. Her belief in her body never wavered, and she is so proud of her birth.

Sometimes a woman may have a concurrent medical history or a pregnancy complication that arises, which does mean that we need to collaborate and birth in a hospital. For some women, this might mean a change in hospital, or it might mean I accompany the couple to the hospital in a support role. Once the birth occurs, I facilitate discharge home as soon as possible, regaining the normalisation of birth. Again, once home, the power is returned to her, enabling the commencement of her early parenting journey. In Australia, 20 weeks gestation is a common time for women to have their first appointment with the doctors. It's fairly standard for women with any highlighted risk, in accordance with hospital guidelines, to have a doctor's appointment to give approval for a chosen model of care. I find it's at this time that many clients come to me having been disappointed with lack of choices or denied the chosen care options.

This client called me at 30 weeks, having been diagnosed with GDDM (gestational diabetes diet controlled) and also hoping for a VBAC. She had previously had an emergency cesarean four years prior. She said she left each appointment feeling deflated and less positive about her chances of VBAC. She had hired a doula to support her hospital birth; it was this doula that suggested she investigate the option of homebirth. We met soon after and started the new direction. She had a wonderfully powerful and life-changing home waterbirth of her son as her husband and daughter watched on. That doula has now booked me for her own birth.

The ability to allow birth to unfold without concern for time changes the dynamic. I see amazing things come when birthing is left alone. My colleagues and I see that labour patterns are unique. Some women have times of 'rest ', surges stop or slow, and when ready, the birth picks up again, and a baby is born. In the fear-based system, these deviations are treated as a red flag, and a risk would be assumed; the resulting intervention then resulting in an interruption in the normal physiological hormones of birth.

A couple transferred care to me at around 28 weeks. She had begun to feel lost on the system at her local hospital. She had gone into her first birth contentedly naïve, happy to 'go with the flow', a common statement in this country. Whilst she had a vaginal birth, it left her feeling vulnerable and weak, rather than the strong new mum she had envisioned.

We set the pool up in her bedroom, where she practiced sitting in the pool, meditating on the birth she desired. She laboured beautifully, her husband in the pool behind supporting her back. After a few hours, her sounds disappeared; Jasmine went silent. We sat in awe as she peacefully and silently used her breath to conquer transition. After about one hour, she suddenly told us he was coming, another surge, and she reached down to show us the baby was ready and there. The next surge, she lifted her new son up onto her chest.

In my practice, one forth of my clients are first-time mums. Of the rest, some are repeat homebirths, but most are coming to home birth after a hospital birth. Two-thirds of these women come to me aiming for VBAC. Some are traumatised, and some just felt let down and like a failure by having a cesarean. Others feel extremely strongly that they had been failed by the system and have a powerful drive to achieve VBAC not only for themselves but to show those that doubted them the first time. I never make a judgement on the previous care given; it is impossible to know exactly what happened without actually being present in that birth room. I can, however, gain an understanding of the process of that labour, and a picture as to what might have contributed. Most commonly, I see the cascade of intervention leading to a time limit being reached, a baby becoming tired due to the intervention, and birth absolutely needing to be facilitated. Currently, over 30% of first-time mums are induced in Australia; of those, a very high percentage go on to need a cesarean section. Sadly, I see women being set up to fail again, booked in for a second induction – particularly risky for VBAC women. Statistics suggest 75% of women should be able to achieve a VBAC. Depending on the institution, most sit around a 30% success rate in Australia. At home, we have a near 100% success rate. I believe the three biggest factors in this are: firstly, a known carer, secondly, no inductions, and thirdly we treat VBAC births the same as any home birth: without fear. Current hospital practice uses a fear/risk-based approach requiring strict monitoring and timelines, removal of access to birth pools, and food/drink. The newest guidelines contraindicate these practices, but sadly they are still practiced routinely. Women are sharing this information. Social media platforms are full of women giving and receiving information and advice about VBAC.

Bringing birth back home allows for individualised care. It allows women to be at the centre of the care. Maternity units are focused on the system, and midwives working within them are bound by hospital policies and guidelines. Homebirth allows midwives to fully support women to make informed choices, improving outcomes and making the most of the true physiological nature that is birth. Many women have told me that they would never have achieved their normal birth if not for being in their own homes away from the pressures of the hospital. They talk of the fear created by being hooked up to monitors and drips, and interventions impacting the unfolding of the natural hormones of labour. Birth occurs best where women feel safest: for many, this is their HOME. I will never work anywhere but home-birth again. It is a magical thing. I witness pure exhilaration on women's faces. I see strength shine and damage disappear. On one Christmas Eve, I witnessed an HBAC in the early hours of the morn. As she reached down to bring her baby up out of the birth pool; the words came immediately "I am not broken anymore."

KARYN BESLEY

Karyn Besley is a Privately Practicing Endorsed Midwife (PPEM) in Australia. As a PPEM, she attends homebirth to a caseload of 40-50 women per year. This model provides full continuity of care 24/7. Karyn is mother to 4 sons.

Social Media
Website www.hunterhomebirth.com.au
Email. info@hunterhomebirth.com
Facebook Hunter Homebirth Midwife in Private Practice
Instagram @hunterhomebirth

3

A TALE OF TWO BIRTHS

LUCIA STUART

Homebirth! What an experience. If only I had known with my first birth that a positive, powerful, and empowering maternity journey and birth was possible. I am a massive advocate for homebirth, so much so that I believe homebirth should be brought back home as a first choice, so let's see if I can try and take a little of the magic from my birth and put it in writing for you.

Failed induction, emergency c section

I am a mother of two girls born 19 months apart. My first was born in November 2018, and my second in July 2020. My first birth was an emergency cesarean due to a failed induction, and my second a home birth. I live in Australia and experienced two very different maternity and birth journeys, and this is my story.

On the television, from speaking to new mums, talking to our grandparents, friends, family. Birth is bad—many a joke based on the pain of childbirth. What you will learn from my experience is that the biggest kept secret is that it's not that birth is painful; it's that women are powerful, never has there been a more accurate quote.

Looking back now, I see that I had never actually met anyone with a positive natural birth experience. All of these women around me had traumatic experiences. I now see all of them experienced birth trauma, the angry part. Most of it was avoidable had they not been a victim to the system. They didn't advise me about birth because they hadn't known, they had never been empowered to birth their baby, birth was bad, and you just got through it, an unlucky part of being a woman. The only positive stories I had were of those who had an epidural, so it makes sense I would remember that right, of course. As birth came closer, I ignored all the bad epidural stories and only focused on the positive ones since natural birth wasn't an option, right? Why would I when it all sounded so scary and painful without? You don't get a medal for not having pain relief, right? As long as the baby is born healthy?

More than ever, I now realise how important personal research is and how important birth itself is. I remember having an appointment with a midwife and asking if there are any antenatal classes available. She said to me, there are these ones with the hospital, but really, birth is one day of your life, there's not much to it, the only good thing about the classes is you get a tour of the hospital. This woman was a mum and a midwife at the obstetrician practice but also worked shifts at the local hospital, and I now realise how damaging that information and attitude towards birth is. Women need to know how their body works, what to expect; basically hypnobirthing for every woman. But I guess an informed pregnant Mum isn't as simple as they wouldn't accept the standard "care"! I still went to the antenatal class at the hospital, and I didn't learn much. We watched a lady birthing on her back and learnt what pain relief options would be available to us, oh and how to put a nappy on a doll. There and then, I made the decision I would have the epidural as soon as possible. My husband William and I even (shamefully and ignorantly) laughed about why the hell would you go through agony when you didn't have to? I researched the hell out of pregnancy, breastfeeding, postpartum, Montessori. I put little thought into the birth because, as that midwife said, it's only one day of your life that we have to grin and bear.

Long story short, I ended up being induced at 37 weeks due to an appointment with a maternal-fetal medicine specialist team and being told that people with autoimmune issues have a higher rate of a stillborn past 37 weeks. After this meeting, I advocated for that induction myself. I mean, these medical professionals are telling me I'm putting my baby at risk if I don't have the baby before 38 weeks. My pregnancy was a unicorn pregnancy, with no morning sickness at all, no issues. I, in fact, didn't even feel pregnant, I went hiking and bike riding in Europe in early pregnancy, and I was able to resume my fitness regime throughout. The baby was growing consistently, even though the baby was on the more petite end in size. I went in to get my induction with the foley balloon, and I have never ever felt agony worse than the balloon being inserted. It was a night of hell. The next day, they took the balloon out, and I was barely 3cm dilated, and my cervix was still long and hard. I couldn't believe it. I was sure I would be 5/6cm after the night I had! They broke my waters which were also agonisingly painful and a timely process, using all sorts of tools to break them. I was hooked up to the syntocin drip, and contractions started. I did move around for a while, pulling the drip along with me. I got that epidural as soon as I could. My body wasn't ready to birth, and my baby wasn't ready to be born.

Well, I had what I thought was a severe reaction to the epidural; swollen, shaking, lockjaw. Apparently, this is normal. They don't tell you about these side effects, do they? So it wasn't a surprise that out of all of these days, to prematurely put my body into labour, I didn't progress, and I ended up with a cesarean. I was relieved to have it all over, to be honest. I was also happy to have multiple copies of my birth plan laminated, to try and ensure skin to skin and other things that I knew were important. During the operation, I felt nauseous.

The anesthetist was so beautiful to me and was on it right away. The surgeons and midwives were joyful and upbeat, and this did give me some enthusiasm. I remember the midwife who was next to me. I only met her as I was wheeled into the operating theatre. She was called Hannah. I was pretty drugged up, and I found comfort as that's my sister's name, except my sister's name does not have h on the end. Yes, I remember thinking about that, and it gave me comfort when I felt so unwell and surreal.

I did get skin to skin as soon as she was born. I remember thinking how beautiful she was. Jasmine Florence Stuart was born, and she was tiny, weighing 2.7kg (5.9 lb). I didn't want to hold her as I felt so unwell and overwhelmed, but then I remember thinking, I better hold her, or they will think I'm not a suitable mother. My mind went to some crazy places! I just wanted to sit up, but they were stitching me back together. I kept saying, "I'll be ok if I can just sit up." Finally, I asked William to please hold her. I was then taken to recovery while William had the baby. I found out that poor William had been left sitting on a chair on his own with a baby. My very smart husband noticed that my little girl was sucking on her swaddle, meaning she was trying to latch, which he had learned from the breastfeeding workshop we did with an IBCLC (International Board Certified Lactation Consultant). When he was allowed to come in, Jasmine latched right away, and it was a dream. I luckily had researched so much about breastfeeding that I was able to exclusively breastfeed my baby. It amazes me that midwives have little knowledge of breast-feeding. I knew that colostrum was the perfect food for my baby until my milk came in, yet they offered formula so we could sleep. I knew that cluster feeding was an essential part of the natural and successful breastfeeding cycle and that the intervention of giving formula so early could have sabotaged my entire breastfeeding jour-ney, which was important to me.

I regretted allowing visitors. It was a constant stream of visitors, for three days straight, many people I don't see that often, so why on earth would I want to see them when I was at my most vulnerable! I acknowledge this visitors at the hospital tradition is very much expected, but I now see that maybe this needs to change. There were kids shaking beds and my baby being handed around constantly. I missed some of the mini-classes they provided due to visitors. I certainly don't blame the visitors, this is very much a standard practice of which may work for some, just not me. I believe now, the hospital or the first week (or two) is not the time for visitors, especially those who just want to see a baby and aren't close to the birthing mother. It is such a sacred time and only suitable for your very closest. William and I were woken up from a well-needed sleep on a few occasions due to unexpected visitors just rocking up. I knew next time, no visitors, and next time, if people just turned up, they would be turned away, no matter who they were.

I don't think I was strong enough at that time, but don't you worry, mama bear may have taken a few days to come out, but when she did, a mama was born, and the connection to Jasmine was nothing like I have ever experienced. I never knew a love like it. William, Jasmine, and I created so much oxytocin. Safe to say, we all bonded, the three of us, Jasmine and I, Jasmine and William, and William and I bonded deeper than I thought possible. We have always been besties, two peas in a pod, and soul mates but wowee, so much oxytocin around the entire fourth trimester. My biggest 'mum guilt' about that birth is that I let her go to the nursery when they asked what I wanted. I knew the skin to skin was so important, but I jumped at the chance. I was excited to sleep, so safe to say there was nothing natural about the birth, and with the knowledge I have now, it all happened unnecessarily, and that is what makes me angry. I experienced everything you just read when my pregnancy was going just perfect, all tests and scans, perfect, and there was no reason to induce me. Yes, I made a decision, but it certainly wasn't informed. You need all the information to make an informed decision, I realised I was traumatised by the experience when I started the hypnobirthing course with my next pregnancy. I mean if it had been a true emergency, but it was all unnecessary, that makes me angry. How broken the system is.

The second I left that hospital it was happily ever after. Or was it?

HBAC: Home Birth After Cesarean

10 months later, I was running my business from home, while baby-wearing my baby as she is totally a koala. I deal with pregnant ladies, new mums, and kind of live, breath, and work babies! So of course, I'm pregnant again! Meaning my children will be 2 under 2! The first thing I did was book into the GP to get my referral to an obstetrician. And repeat the cycle right! This time a female obstetrician, who spouted the usual, ah yes, you will be fine for a VBAC (vaginal birth after cesarean). Which considering what I'd read on some VBAC social media groups with many women being told they will have to have an elective C-section due to the close gap and the fact they had a C-section. I didn't consider my C-section traumatic at this stage, and I didn't know yet that the reason I had a C-section was unnecessary. This time, I did myself a favour, as I was scared of birth, and decided to enroll into a HypnoBirthing course at the Newcastle Birth Movement, such a great service. Well, this is where my world was turned upside down. I was going to this course to learn how to tolerate pain. What I learnt was, there is no pain, there are interventions that disrupt your body doing what it was built to do, birth! Each disruption stops and starts birth. I learnt about my body, I learnt true birth education. I now knew the only detriment to an effective, physiological birth, was that hospital. So, I planned to birth at home for as long as I could and then go in. My only worry was the car ride to the hospital disturbing my birth progress, for an undisturbed birth, makes enough endorphins that are more amazing than any drug. At this stage, I'm seeing that it's the medical interventions and the disruptions that mean women are birthing without natural endorphins, nor do they know what their body is doing; I certainly didn't. A week

before I did the hypnobirthing, I met a woman who had had an HBAC (Home Birth After Cesarean). I didn't even know homebirth was an option, and I remember thinking it was a little out there, and birth needs to be safely in the hospital. How wrong I was.

During my HypnoBirthing class, other mums were birthing at a public birth centre, I had never even heard of this option, I was booking into a private hospital, I now see that being in a private health fund is a curse in the birthing world, the only benefit being your partner can stay at the hospital with you your entire stay. Once I started to learn about birth, true birth, how the body actually works vs the antenatal classes at the hospital, how the hormones work, how your body literally opens, hips widen, my state of mind, was from, how will I endure pain, to, how will I work with my body, something clicked.

I started looking into a private homebirth midwife in my area as I wouldn't be eligible for the publicly funded homebirth due to my previous C-section. That's when I emailed the (now I know) famous Karyn Besely from Hunter Home Birth, you should be able to read her journey in this book.

Initially, my husband and I felt it was too expensive for our budget, we had already spent a lot of money on our private health fund which wouldn't cover this. I didn't consider it again as an option, because, to be honest, I still at this stage did not value myself or see my pregnancy, my birth, or my experience as worthy of such an expense. As time went on, my husband felt such a strong passion about considering the homebirth option and he said, let's meet with Karyn, we will find the money. If that's the only issue we have, then he wants me to have the best. I mean you will easily spend a considerable amount more money on a wedding, but not your birth? So we made the decision to meet up with Karyn and see what we think. I was 20 weeks pregnant here.

As soon as we met her, we knew. She was busy, gentle, kind, and professional yet I could see a flare of personality shining through with the subtle fashion statements, like her scarf and boots. Her knowledge was out of this world, yet she appeared human. At this stage I was due for an appointment with the obstetrician, you know the usual robotic medical experience you get in those places. There's so much I would say about this first meeting, but we don't have all day. Safe to say, and this is a chapter, not the whole book, I left that first meeting knowing, this was the only missing piece of the puzzle, that birth isn't scary, birth can be magical. Continuity of care.

From that moment on, I changed over to Karyn, and my appointments were now in the comforts of my own home. What a relief this was with a 15-month-old and unlike my first pregnancy, morning sickness in my first and third trimester, and lots of normal pregnancy ailments. It was just brilliant. Karyn brought all of her equipment and spent a lot of time at each appointment. I just felt so safe. If I had a question, I could text or call her, and she always responded. Her advice and assistance were always above and beyond. My husband was invited into the magical antenatal space with welcome arms, instead of being a bloke in the way. Don't get me going about this. My husband was certainly not respected with my first birth, which in turn, made me not comfortable. I could never have imagined such care, and when I divide the fee of the Private Midwife by the hours spent on me, it far outweighs a minimum wage. It just shows how passionate a private midwife is about the birthing mother. Karyn was gentle but also assertive and tough in nature. It gave me the security I needed, she knew all of the up to date information.

Only a few weeks after changing over, COVID hit. Lockdowns began and partners were not allowed to attend appointments in Hospitals. Doulas weren't even allowed to attend the birth. Even the publicly funded birth centres and homebirths were having these restrictions. Never was I happier to have changed over. I must have been the luckiest pregnant woman in the world during this time, and me not qualifying for the birth centre/public-funded home birth was such a blessing. I wouldn't have coped without Williams' support.

We were all in lockdown so it meant I had my husband at home and able to help me during the third trimester. I had a really beautiful time in my maternity bubble with no visitors to entertain. I used this time to go walking in nature, in an oxytocin love bubble, with no obligations or commitments to anyone but my little family. Not one negative or impersonal medical appointment. 40 weeks came and went. 41 weeks came and went. People started calling, texting, instant messaging, and I started to get stressed wondering would I need to go to the hospital, even though the pregnancy was tracking so well? I knew from birth education, that you're not overdue until after 42 weeks and that many women don't birth at 38/39/40.

Had I been in the public system, I would have been pressured to induce again, or even have a repeat C-section, even though the baby was growing perfectly and I was coping well. So, I used from 40 weeks on to really create my birth space; get out in nature, not watch the news. What was funny is, I was convinced at 37 weeks I would go early. My belly had dropped, then again, I was adamant my baby was a boy. Throughout, Karyn supported me, looked after me and let me know what my options were. Some of the most magical moments I have are from 40-42 weeks. I wrote some birth yoga, HypnoBirthing, and positive affirmation blogs. It was kind of a way to revise what I had learnt in preparation for my own birth, as well as share that knowledge during the height of covid. I had many pregnant customers, new mums, in tears to me via my business as they were suffering in lockdown, unable to socialise on their maternity leave and having no support for such intimate appointments during pregnancy. So I angled it all around preparing for birth may it be a hospital or home birth in the comfort of your home. I also felt so lucky that all of my experience was in the safety of my own home with the support of my husband, daughter and dog.

I fondly remember bushwalking also known as bush waddling, while my husband wore our toddler on his back at a beautiful place called Wangi Wangi in NSW Australia, a magical place to walk. I remember I was 41 weeks and a few days and something in me just surrendered and I truly felt it. I'm trusting my body as we learnt in HypnoBirthing. My body knows what it needs to do, and my body is doing all of the work it needs to prepare my body and my baby to birth effectively and smoothly. 42 weeks on the dot, I felt some Braxton hicks, like I got most nights from about 37 weeks. I woke up in the middle of the night with consistent mild contractions. They were more powerful than I expected for early labour. I tried to sleep through them, but couldn't. I was also having a bloody show. Ball time! My daughter was asleep, I woke my husband to let him know. I'd watched so many birth videos, and if I learnt anything from HypnoBirthing; you will birth when you birth.

So, a text to Karyn and I put on my HypnoBirthing meditation; the last semester of my pregnancy I listened to this one track before I went to sleep. I never got to the end of it, because it always put me to sleep. I wish I had discovered this track when I first got pregnant as I suffered from insomnia the entire time! Back to my early labour, the hypnobirthing soundtrack, I couldn't relax through with it. So off that went. I had some relaxing music in the background and just breathed through them, in my mind, imagining my cervix opening with the contraction. It was quite amazing really. Once daylight hit, we called my family to come to pick up my daughter. The plan was for my sister to stay in a hotel close by during the birth. I knew I wouldn't be able to truly let go if my daughter was with me, even though I kind of hoped I'd be able to have her there. As the day continued, I kept moving, dancing with William, in between the contractions of course. I thought I might like a bath, bad idea, this was extremely claustrophobic, so the trustee old shower, my yoga ball, and the breathing I had learnt in birth yoga. Regular check-ins and visits from Karyn. With contractions coming every five minutes, about late lunchtime,

Karyn said we can start to fill up the pool if we liked. During each contraction, I literally couldn't lie on my back, I had to be on all fours or leaning over something. I couldn't walk, talk or move during a contraction. I just breathed. My main breathing was the J breath during each contraction. I had planned on using other breathing techniques for certain parts of my labour, but the J breath felt the best.

I could literally visualise each contraction of my baby moving down, cervix softening and opening. I got into the birth pool late afternoon and my gosh it was magic. I have the most wonderful vision later in the night of Karyn sat in a corner knitting, candles flickering, music relaxing. Karyn randomly trickled water over my back in a spot that was amazing; the only touch I could endure and welcome during a contraction. Oh and this entire time I was so hot so she would provide a washcloth in ice-cold water.

I remember Karyn putting a cloth on my head, and I said, "omg this smells amazing," it was the most comforting relaxing smell. I asked her what it was. She said, "it's your body and room lavender spray," I laughed and started saying to William, "omg this is the spray I stock in my business that is pre-packed birth bundles." I committed to writing a blog about this moment. To this day, I tell customers of this moment; in between contractions talking work strategy. On that note, I even packed bundles for a few customer orders early on because I wanted them perfect. It's really funny what matters during this time.

William was having a rest for the first time since two nights prior, even though he said he was ok. I was kind of happy on my own in that pool. I insisted and near right demanded he rests because he will need it. But being in the birth pool slowed down the labour; contractions slowed down. I decided to take some Panadeine Forte and attempt a little nap, as I was feeling a little fatigued. I was coping just fine, in between contractions, having a laugh or just chilling. I never ever felt rushed. I was safe, I felt loved, respected. The entire time we had the most beautiful music playlist playing throughout the house, "a warning from the elders" by Brian Metcalfe. I had more playlists ready, but this resonated with me so much. It was peaceful, and there was no rush. I kept my water intake with coconut water. I was able to sleep, but every 5-7 minutes a contraction would come, and I could not physically lie down on my side, even though the little microsleeps in between were so comfy on my side. It gave William and Karyn a chance to sleep too. A few hours passed; the morning was here. I used the morning to try and keep moving. I knew everything was working; time and these things can't be rushed. I got back into the birth pool, and again paradise. But guess what happened, my contractions slowed down again, keeping in mind we are getting to the afternoon heading into my third night of no real sleep.

Karyn called in her assisting midwife (Jess) to relieve her and change things up. Jess was heavily pregnant, and this would be her last birth before her own birth, which was nice to know.

We carried on doing our thing. I found sitting on the toilet backwards really got things going, but I also enjoyed changing to the shower and the yoga ball on the bed. I remember a moment speaking to William, saying, "I don't know how much longer I can do this," and like it was every five minutes for how many days. If it didn't liven up by the night, I needed to discuss my options, I kept manifesting on something that Karyn had said earlier, and that was that I was still in early labour, not active labour. I mean surely not, but then again, you don't get those lovely endorphins until you're in active labour. I wanted to go back into the pool as I was coping well. I started to feel a little deflated when I was in the pool. I loved being in that pool, but I could feel it was slowing down the contractions again, this is when I felt fed up.

Karyn came back and I discussed what I was thinking--William was really supporting me and telling me I was doing a great job; that I could do this. I said, "I am coping with the contractions, but I'm just so fatigued." I asked if Karyn would check how dilated I was. This would be the first vaginal exam since I changed from the obstetrician to private midwife. Of course, she said yes. Flashbacks of the vaginal exams I've had previously in mind, but I kind of had said to myself; if I'm not 5cm at least, I'm going to have to consider the hospital.

The last time I failed to progress, which ended up in a cesarean and this was double the time. I tell you now, Karyn made my bed a sterilised location and treated me with so much respect; it sounds odd writing this, but the biggest thing that shocked me, and at the time; I felt slightly embarrassed, was the consent, she asked me before doing anything; I remember saying yes, of course, you can. Not one bit of pain did I occur. Karyn said I was 4cm enthusiastically, and that my cervix was so soft and short. During my previous induction, I had gotten to 5 cm. Karyn, and then Jess, and then William, were so enthusiastic. I remember looking at William. He believed in me. Something clicked and I decided this was it. It's on. I accepted my first big intervention and that was to have my waters broke and a sweep. Previously, this experience was absolutely agonising. There was not even a single pain this time! It certainly got things going.

I knew if my waters were broken, I was going to give birth. It was kind of a commitment to myself, my baby, and my husband who was the most amazing birth partner. He was loving, kind, helpful, present, and welcome in my sacred space. Thinking of him now makes my heart melt.

Soon after a pre-arranged chiropractor, organised by Jess arrived after I had said I would be up for something like that. It was a bit odd as I didn't know her. I kept apologising in between contractions, she was very kind and understanding. It was like a little tool up my sleeve that I valued coming into my home. The late afternoon came, darkness was coming,

William and the midwives ordered Thai food. I decided to come downstairs and the atmosphere was so normal, that I just laboured over the couch, over the benchtop, the lighting in the home was perfect; having a tech-savvy husband has its benefits, this is when the magic began. William was so supportive, I felt the love that Karyn was still with me. The nighttime came. I remembered my last birth. My cervix was long and hard when they started the induction, and just before we accepted a cesarean, the midwife checked my dilation, a few hours after the obstetrician had, and she said 5cm was pushing it.

My homebirth, I knew I had gotten this far on my own. I decided to hit the footpath and walk around the complex. William by my side. Stopping mid-step for a contraction. Up some steps. Wooo, the contractions were building up. I continued the J breaths. It was like meditation in a way. Then I projectile vomited all in the garden of a random garden. William attempted to usher me on. I said no way, we waited out the contraction and made our way back to the house. I do laugh back at the memories of every update, even my vomit. Karyn would say, yes! That's great! That's good! I think her empathy and support vs sympathy, kept me in the game. I made it upstairs and I remember this moment clearly. I even have a photo of it. The only overpowering moment of discomfort was around my bum and hips; the photo shows a big bone sticking out; now knowing it's the "Rhombus of Michaelis" when the hips open. I kind of screamed, and I was saying to Karyn, "I'm sorry," she said, "you want to scream, scream, you want to shout, you shout; it is happening."

It was the permission that I needed. I let it all loose. I roared through back to back contractions, and then boom endorphins. Each contraction brought on a burst of bliss. They said I could get in the pool now if I wished as the warm water had been added. I didn't know how I'd move rooms to get there, but I did. Each contraction so wild; the absolute peace in between each contraction. I knew this was good. I wanted William's touch even during contractions. The pool reflected on the roof due to the flickering candles and the music of "a warning from the elders" was amazing. At some point, it changed to African drumming. The midwives were around, but not in my way or intrusive, doing checks as they needed on babies heartbeat, etc.

All of a sudden, my body's intense involuntary pushing began. I said, "my body is pushing. I literally am not," it was amazing. Each natural push, accompanied by the stillest, calmest, bliss I have ever experienced. William holding onto my hand. I had no doubt. Hypno-Birthing taught me everything. This was happening; my body was birthing my baby. A most magnificent moment; when the head started to birth, I still remember that feeling so fondly, I couldn't wait for the next contraction because at this stage every push and every pause between was magical, not in any way painful. My body made the endorphins it was built to make. I only felt the burning ring of fire people describe for a short time because my body kicked in and did its thing. I used my J breath and a low roar with each contraction. And then, my baby was born before midnight on the third night since this all began. It was 30 minutes from transition to baby born. I didn't catch my baby as I had planned. Karyn handed the baby right over and I lifted the baby out of the water. Before I even looked at the face, I checked if the baby was a girl or boy. I was absolutely shocked it was a girl because I was so sure it was a boy due to the pregnancy being so different. Then I felt pure joy as I loved the baby name my husband and I had picked out; Apollonia Aurelia Stuart. Two little girls. I was instantly in love. So in love. I missed not having Jasmine there. I missed her so much. I held Apollonia in my arms in the birth pool, surrounded with love, kindness, and care. My mind was so clear. What was amazing about this birth was it wasn't surreal; it was so real, it was empowering, I was strong and clear-minded afterwards.

I was able to Facetime and chatter. I wasn't drugged up. The birth of the placenta was just fine. I did feel a slight bit of nausea during that. This was the first time I felt nauseous this whole time, so I asked William if he would like to hop in. Before I finished the sentence, his shirt was off, and he was in. I got him to hold Apollonia. It was special and we were all connected in that birth pool. Once the placenta was birthed, I was amazed to see it, as I hadn't seen my first one. I felt amazing. I just walked from the birth pool to my lovely comfy bed. I did need a couple of stitches downtown, but it was done so professionally and did not change the atmosphere.

After some time, the cord was cut. Apollonia was weighed at a whooping 3.83kg, which was such a difference from Jasmine's 2.7kg, yet she looked so tiny still. I didn't swaddle Apollonia and we slept well that night. I woke up feeling absolutely amazing. It was all cemented when Jasmine met Apollonia. We were all together. Apollonia may not have been a unicorn pregnancy, but she is a unicorn baby; wise beyond her years, happy birth, happy baby? Or just luck?

Homebirth was the birth that didn't need a birth plan because my private midwife was all on board with knowledge and experience, continuity of care. I will forever be grateful for Karyn. She is a true angel in human form and she made it possible to experience such magic.

While I'm not anti-hospital, because the hospital definitely has its place in birth; for emergencies and such. I believe that the promoted option of home birth should be normalised. Many countries in Europe, homebirth is a very normal thing. A birthing woman isn't sick. She doesn't need to be a patient in a hospital bed like a weak and fragile sick person. She needs support and expertise by her side. Hospitals are for the care for sick people, not a positive natural event. A birthing mother isn't a helpless soul unable to birth their baby. I always find it insane people say the obstetricians "deliver" your baby, they don't.

People think homebirth is extreme. When people heard I had a home birth, I got all of the wow, you're strong, I couldn't do it, good on you but not for me. Out of these stories, what sounds extreme to you? To make an informed decision, you need to know the information exists. Even though I said the word yes to everything with my first birth, I didn't know the true options. If you were looking for a sign, here's the sign. You won't regret it. I was more cared for than I could have ever imagined. The six weeks of aftercare was so positive and lovely and in the comforts of our own home.

My newborn bubble was divine. I chose not to have any visitors other than a few close family members this time. I got to experience my rite of passage. It was the birth, that once I held my baby in that birth pool, I couldn't wait to have another. Therefore, I genuinely believe and have experienced what birth can be like if birth was brought back home.

LUCIA STUART

Lucia Stuart loves life, loves her children, and loves her husband. Born in England but raised in Australia, Lucia worked in the public sector before starting her own business following the birth of her first baby in 2018. Birth and becoming a mother taught her so much. About her body, about babies, about the medical system, and most importantly, about life. Now that she is enlightened about what a positive birth experience can be, she is committed to sharing her story, her experiences, and helping other mama's, expecting or not to take back control over their own birthing journey.

Social Media links
Facebook: @bundlebags https://www.facebook.com/bundlebags/
Instagram: @bundlebags https://www.instagram.com/bundlebags/
Email: lucia.stuart@bundlebags.com.au
Website: https://bundlebags.com.au/

STORIES FROM

NORTH
AMERICA

4

MANIFESTING MY DREAM BIRTH
HOSPITAL VBAC TO HOME BIRTH VBAC

CORINNE BROWN

THE BIRTH of my third and final baby took place at home, and it was profoundly empowering for me. Not only because of the birth itself—which was the most magical three hours of my life—but also because of how it forced me to take full accountability for my own experience and speak my truth. I had to advocate hard for my home birth or risk losing the opportunity to have one altogether.

Pressure In Birth

If you are planning a home birth, you know it inherently comes with some level of pressure for your birth to go smoothly. But when it came to my home birth, there was even more pressure because of the work I do in the world, how my *first* home birth attempt went down, and everything else going on in my life at the time.

As far as the work I do in the world, I am a former Naturopathic Doctor, Founder & CEO of my online business, Brownroots Love, and Creator of the natural birth preparation program, Love Your Labour©, which has now helped thousands of women successfully achieve their dream births. Between my program and my Natural Labour Prep Webinar (which you can watch for free on my website), over the years, I have trained tens of thousands of women to have positive natural birth experiences.

So now that I was pregnant again and aiming for a VBAC[1] home birth, all eyes were on me. My whole community was waiting with bated breath to hear my successful birth story. This loving social pressure kept me accountable–I had to walk my talk and prove that the Love Your Labour© system legitimately worked. No pressure!

In addition to the well-intentioned pressure from my tribe, my *first* home birth attempt also loomed in the back of my mind.

The Unplanned Hospital Detour

Before I was even pregnant, I knew I wanted a home birth. So on November 2nd, 2011, after 12 hours of natural labor with my first baby, my water broke . . . and then my heart broke, too. I noticed that there was meconium[2] in the fluid, and I knew this meant I was no longer a good candidate for a home birth.

After the midwife arrived, she confirmed my suspicions and called for an ambulance transfer to the hospital. There, we discovered my baby was in the frank breech position[3]. I labored on, praying between contractions for a successful vaginal breech delivery, but the stars did not align. Or perhaps they did because what happened next changed the trajectory of my life and business forever . . .

After 12 more hours of laboring at the hospital, with no progress beyond my initial 5 cm check, I was labelled 'Failure To Progress'. Defeated and heartbroken, I signed the cesarean consent forms, and Rowan was born via c-section.

I tried to wing a home birth. I was so confident and fearless (perhaps also a tad cocky and naive) that I didn't prepare my body for birth. I never considered needing to transfer to the hospital; *I didn't even pack a hospital bag!* So I was basically in shock throughout this entire unplanned hospital detour.

In my state of dumbfounded disbelief, I unintentionally received many unwanted medical interventions. Hospital gown and mesh underwear, IV fluids, external fetal monitoring - all within the first 20 minutes of arriving. Those things may seem small and insignificant, but I immediately went from feeling like a healthy laboring woman to a terrified hospital patient with a medical issue. I was completely unprepared to advocate for myself in this scenario, and as a result, I received the domino effect of interventions and slid straight down the Labor Funnel[4].

As a Prenatal Naturopathic Doctor and Labor Doula who had told everyone and their dog about her plan for a home birth, my ego and confidence took a major hit. The whole experience left a physical and emotional scar that took time to fully integrate and heal.

VBAC Redemption

After my C-section, I became determined to avoid the same experience again the next time around. I researched naturopathic protocols to optimize the birth process, and I then compiled them into a system called the "Four Step Natural Labour Prep System" for my pregnant patients.

By 2015 when I became pregnant with my second baby, I had seen this system work wonders. I knew I had to follow it myself AND make it easier for other women to follow, too. I transformed my in-person system into an online offering which has now become my flagship natural labor prep program, Love Your Labour©, or LYL.

For my second labor, I followed the LYL program, and it allowed me to successfully achieve my VBAC by overcoming some bumps along the way. While creating LYL, I was *thoroughly* preparing my body and mind for this birth–and it paid off! Kyle and I labored at home together for several hours and arrived at the hospital 6 cm dilated. I was already further along than I ever got with my first labor. My confidence was restored!

This experience was pretty much ideal as far as hospital births go. For my entire hospital stay, it was only me, Kyle and my midwife in the room. I never saw a nurse or Obstetrician once. I wanted to keep this birth ultra low tech because I knew that was the best way to avoid unwanted medical interventions. This time I was much more prepared and empowered to advocate for myself: I wore my own beautiful labor gown, declined an IV, labored GBS[5] unknown, and chose intermittent auscultation[6] instead of being tethered to the external fetal monitoring machine.

Because I had spent the last several months creating Love Your Labour© with all its step-by-step protocols to avoid the Labor Funnel, I was prepared to prevent obstacles and deal with issues as they came up. In the end, there were a few minor interventions, and it wasn't perfect, but I was proud as heck of my all natural 14 hour VBAC.

Although it was a positive hospital birth, it was a hospital birth nonetheless. I still had to leave my house, drive to the hospital, find parking, get checked in, labor in a strange place with strange smells and sounds, distractions, and harsh lights—not at all conducive to labor! I knew in my heart that this experience had the potential to be so much more intimate than that. I was happy to have achieved my VBAC with Harvey, but it only sharpened my desire for a completely natural comfy-cozy blissed-out home birth someday.

Home Is Where Birth Works Best

Two years after my VBAC, I took a trip to Tennessee to visit The Farm, where Ina May Gaskin and The Farm Midwives worked since the 1970s. This Farm adventure was on my bucket list for years, so in May 2017, I took the plunge and signed up for a Midwifery Assistant Training course. Although I already believed in home birth, this trip gave me an unshakeable validation that home is without a doubt the safest and most normal place to birth. It's where we were designed to deliver!

The Societal Birth Bias[7] says that home birth is unsafe, but that is simply untrue. Home is where you can fully be in your power! Where else can you feel safe enough to let your inner Badass Birth Goddess out and really get *into* it? Much like with achieving an orgasm, feeling afraid and tense doesn't work! To be able to surrender fully, safety and privacy are non-negotiable. Giving birth at home lets those juices flow, which allows your labor to unfold smoothly and efficiently.

The Farm Midwives anchored my faith that home is where the physiology of birth truly works BEST. Over 40+ years of delivering 10,000+ babies, they have an impressively low 1.5% cesarean rate, which means around 98.5% of births are successfully delivered naturally at home![8]

Our Universe Baby

A couple months after I got home from The Farm, we went on vacation to my family cottage in Prince Edward Island. We reserved the last night for Kyle and me to have a date night—a rare opportunity for us.

After a delicious seafood dinner, we drove to our favourite PEI beach and were dazzled by the most spectacular sunset we'd ever seen. We walked along the shoreline basking in this magical evening and talking about our relationship, our kids, my business, and our life plan. We knew at some point in our future there would probably be another baby and a move to the east coast, but timelines were fuzzy.

This beach was making sweet love to our senses, we were feeling all the feels, and in a twist of oceanside fate, we made a pact with the Universe: if we got pregnant again someday without trying, that would be the sign that it's time to move our family from Ontario to the east coast! We shook on it, and in a synchronistic demonstration of the Universe's excitement about this new life plan, I immediately got stung by a bee! Ow! Wow! Ok! Got it. Thank you. It was settled, then. If we got pregnant again, we would make the move back to my homeland of Nova Scotia.

The very next night, we conceived our third baby.

By the time I realized it, I was eight days late for my period. Since we weren't trying to conceive, I wasn't tracking these things! I only started to clue in because my boobs were getting big and sore. "It can't be," I thought but took a pregnancy test anyway. My heart dropped when it was positive. I cried from shock and overwhelm! I called Kyle, and his response was just a deadpan ". . . stop it." It was funny and validating that he was feeling the same! We were completely stunned. Yes, we made that pact, but we weren't actually ready to show up for it! Yet here we were. We dubbed this our Universe Baby; the message couldn't have been clearer.

I deeply trusted the sign of this pregnancy, and it mattered not that I had no clue how we'd swing it. I had more blind faith than any rational person would that all the convoluted details would click into place when the timing and energy were right. I was showing up in a state of complete surrender to the flow of this exciting time in our lives!

The next nine months were a true demonstration of divine timing and perfect support from the Universe. We were quickly outgrowing our tiny two-bedroom house as a soon-to-be family of five! By the time I was eight months pregnant, we had finished renovating, packing, and staging our house just in time to put it on the market before the baby arrived.

The house sold quickly! Then that sale fell through. Less than a week later, it sold again—at a higher price! Then my husband found a job in Nova Scotia! That job fell through. A few weeks later, he was offered a better position—with a higher salary! It felt like we were hitting a home run with everything the Universe threw at us.

But on top of all this, I was also planning a home birth!

Manifesting My Home Birth

Although I was successfully managing all these things on my plate, I definitely felt the extra pressure on my home birth.

Pressure from the to-do list that comes with moving my family halfway across the country. Pressure from the hopes and expectations of my audience for me to rock this home birth. Pressure from myself to practice what I preach and do the mental, emotional, physical, and spiritual work to manifest this badass birth!

However, birth doesn't work well under pressure. That's exactly *why* I craved to do it at home. Birth, like lovemaking, only works well when there's zero pressure; your body, mind, and spirit must feel safe to let go and do things in your own way, in your own time.

By this point in early 2018, I had been learning about Universal Laws for a few years, and I was becoming very skilled at focusing my energy in order to manifest my desires. So although the pressures were certainly there, I consciously chose not to worry about them. I had to direct my focus and energy in ways that raised my vibration, not lowered it.

I was visualizing, doing yoga, and meditating a few times per day because I knew—despite everything else going on in my life—this birth experience was deeply important to me on a soul level. It was a major personal goal that I had one last opportunity to achieve. If I didn't do the necessary vibrational work to manifest my home birth, I knew I would never forgive myself.

Part of that vibrational work was being unapologetically protective over the energetic bubble I was creating around my precious experience. So protective, in fact, that I had to fire my midwife.

Why I Fired My Midwife

I was not always particularly outspoken, but as a mother and former ND with personal and medical beliefs that fall outside of the mainstream, I had to learn to speak my truth. If standing up for yourself doesn't come naturally to you yet, choosing to home birth will likely change that. When you decide that your birth experience is more important than what other people think, it allows you to advocate for your choices without fear of judgement.

During this final pregnancy, I had a team of three midwives. My primary and secondary midwives, Laura and Asha, were amazing— sisterly, loving, and compassionate. But the third midwife, Philippa, had a rather flat, cold, clinical energy to her. She was more concerned about her facts and stats than my thoughts and feelings. Hoping to avoid any kind of 'medical' vibe at my home birth, I was secretly praying that Philippa would not be on call when I went into labor.

Well, the Universe heard that "secret praying" and gave me an opportunity to stand up and empower myself. I was in my 38-week midwife appointment when Philippa said to me, "Corinne, I want to talk to you. I know your birth is getting close, but I need to tell you that I personally advise against you having a VBAC at home. I feel it's irresponsible considering the increased chance of uterine rupture and the risk of your baby dying if we cannot make it to the hospital in time."

I would have loved to see the look on my face. For her to blatantly dismiss my birth choices like that, as a midwife, so close to my due date, completely without reason, especially using the "your baby could *die*" fear tactic . . . I was flabbergasted.

Clearly, she didn't know who she was talking to. I was a student of the Universe and had been vibrationally preparing for this exact opportunity to fully commit to my desire by bulldozing any obstacle that stood in my way.

She was being irrationally fearful—significantly more fearful than I was. The other two midwives fully supported my birth plan, especially considering I already had a successful VBAC almost three years ago. Like my favourite midwife, Laura, so eloquently put it: there was no reason to believe my body wouldn't just *spit out a baby!* The risk of a negative outcome was extremely low.

I took a deep breath, looked at Philippa, and politely said, "I understand what you're saying, but I'm sorry . . . I don't think you're the right midwife for me. I will agree to be under your care pre and postnatally, but if you're on call when I go into labor, please arrange to have a backup midwife attend instead."

I literally saw her breathe a sigh of relief. I later learned that one of her past clients had a traumatic VBAC home birth experience, so I don't blame her for her feelings. However, I fully stand by my decision in response to them. As a midwife, she should know not to project her own fearful energy into my, or anyone's, birth space. But this gave me the opportunity to stand in my power, be accountable for my birth, and create that firm boundary.

Her vibe did not align with the birth I was manifesting. I was finetuning the energy around it so precisely that her vibration created an unavoidable dissonance. If she was dragging low-frequency nervous energy into my birth, she could bring down the entire operation. I couldn't risk it. This birth meant too much to me!

Once this nagging thorn in the side of my birth was plucked out, I realized she was the one last detail I'd been mentally tripping over. In the back of my mind, I had a fear that she could be on call for my birth and pull the plug on it. She was the one variable I couldn't control, until I could. No more secretly hoping and praying, I put my foot down and made certain she would not be attending my birth under any circumstances.

The moment I stood up for myself and fired her from my home birth, all traces of doubt within me vanished. Now that I'd cleared that one last hurdle out of my way, I went into full-on Badass Birth Goddess mode. This home birth felt locked and loaded. I had zero doubt, all faith. I stayed super present and didn't give those pesky "what if's" any energy. But I *did* pack a hospital bag this time just to show that I *learned* that lesson, thank you very much!

My Badass Home Birth

My birth story began four days before my birth on May 9, 2018. At 39 weeks, I had a membrane sweep, and my cervix was 2 cm dilated and 50 percent effaced–the same as it was the week before. For three days after the sweep, I was having mild contractions that were slowly getting progressively stronger but spaced so far apart that it was silly to time them or get excited. It felt like the world's longest and most annoying prodromal labor.

Sunday, May 13th, was Mother's Day. I chuckled at how perfect it would be to have my dream birth, at home, with my Universe Baby, on *Mother's Day!*

The whole day I had constant cramping that frequently peaked with harder, more intense waves. I was becoming highly emotional, bursting into tears at the most random moments. We had family visiting for Mother's Day, and I was getting hot and irritable. I desperately wanted them to leave! Every few minutes, I'd have to go around the corner to sway, focus and breathe through a few contractions, which were getting closer and definitely stronger, too.

Kyle planned to cook a fancy dinner for my mom and me on Mother's Day, but by 4pm, we vetoed that plan and ordered a pizza instead. We ate dinner and said goodnight to our big boys for the last time as a family of four. My mom took them downstairs to have a sleepover in the spare room, while Kyle and I went upstairs to our room to have our baby.

I adore that concept. Let's just go upstairs and . . . have our baby! In our bed! Where we made him! It feels so down to earth.

By 6pm, we were upstairs all settled into our birth nest. We had mini lights, music, fresh flowers, and I was laboring in a floral soft maxi dress knotted up on one side. I drank my labor tincture tea while doing acupressure on myself.

For the first hour, contractions were consistently 7-10 minutes apart. They were now strong enough to demand my full attention, but I didn't need Kyle yet. He just supported me by playing gopher, photographer, and cheerleader from the sidelines.

By 7pm, things changed quickly. Contractions were coming 5-7 minutes apart, and I absolutely needed Kyle's help now. He performed acupressure for every contraction and coached me through. He and I both thought I was having a really hard time with early labor–ha! Little did we know how quickly this labor was progressing . . .

Quite quickly, in fact. By 8pm, contractions turned another corner, becoming extremely intense, and were 2-5 minutes apart. I was hanging on for dear life! Kyle and I were still in complete denial about this rapid progress because my previous labors were 24 and 14 hours long, respectively. I was only 2 hours in at this point, yet I was roaring through these wild contractions. We hesitated to call the midwife yet because I had false labor with my last birth and we wanted to make sure this was the real deal. Around 8:45pm, we agreed it was time. My favourite midwife, Laura, had *just* come on call (yay!) and said she'd be right over.

After that, everything was a blur. Contractions were coming 1-2 minutes apart, and transition was causing me to become very detached, foggy, and withdrawn. I was mooing like a barn animal, shaking wildly, skin hot to the touch. It's hard to believe as I write these words, but at the time, I was still in denial, thinking, "if Laura tells me I'm 4 cm, I might just jump out the damn window!"

Deep in Labor Land, I was working hard and getting very hot. I eventually noticed something running down my leg. Once again, hilarious to even type these words, but in my transition-induced stupor, I remember thinking, "is my vagina sweating?!" I was clearly not thinking straight because the dripping was actually amniotic fluid! At this point, it dawned on me how deep into this labor I really was. I couldn't even catch my breath between contractions and started to worry that the midwife may not make it in time.

Then we finally saw her headlights pull in the driveway. Kyle said he was going to go let her in the house, and I was like, "NO YOU ARE NOT. SHE CAN COME IN BY HERSELF. DON'T YOU DARE LEAVE ME." Gripping contractions were coming every minute or two now, and the idea of him leaving me was the scariest thing I could imagine. I was barely able to cope WITH his help! After the next contraction, he said, "Corinne, I'll be RIGHT BACK," and bolted downstairs. I yelled after him, "YOU HAVE 60 SECONDS!!!"

He wasn't even gone for 10 seconds before the next contraction was coming, and I lost all control. I started yelllling for him to come back, but halfway through the contraction, I realized I wasn't yelllling the word "Kyle" I was actually puuushing the word "Kyle", and once I realized I was pushing, I yelled louder, which made me push harder, and the *instant* Laura stepped foot inside the front door, my water broke, splashing all over my feet.

Divine timing or what!

She came up the stairs saying, "it's okay, Corinne, I'm here now! Let's move over to the bed so you don't have this baby on the floor. I'm going to run out to my car and get my equipment, no matter what you do on the next contraction, DON'T PUSH!!" and she dashed out of the room.

The hardest thing I've ever done (like way harder than actually pushing!) was *not pushing* during the next contraction. As soon as Laura got back upstairs, she checked my cervix and said I was 9 cm but that my cervix was disappearing by the second. She said on my next contraction that I was free to go ahead and push!

I decided to push in an upright sitting position, and on the next contraction, when the urge came, I gave in and pushed. And IT. FELT. AMAZING. I pushed with the second contraction and felt him come all the way down into my pelvis. The ring of fire burned so much, I didn't think I would be able to push through that pain. Laura looked me square in the eye and said, "Corinne, I know it seems impossible, but this baby's only coming out one way. You need to gather up all your strength and bravery, push into the pain, and you'll have your baby on the next contraction." I pushed a third time, and his head was born. Laura eased his shoulder out, and seconds later, I received my baby!

I still get goosebumps when I think of how empowering those final moments were. I mustered more strength than I knew I even possessed to push through the pain, and came soaring out the other side into *bliss!* I couldn't believe I did it! Or how FAST it was! Or how EASY it was! Or how GOOD I felt! I cried and squealed and giggled uncontrollably. I just couldn't believe it!

This was an ecstatic birth experience. Active labor was 3 hours long, and I pushed for 7 minutes. Kyle cut the cord once it stopped pulsating. It literally could not have possibly gone any smoother. The timing of everything was absolutely impeccable, almost like it was divinely timed down to the last perfect thoughtful detail . . .

After Vance was born, we snuggled in bed for an hour, falling in love completely undisturbed. Kyle and I gushed about how cute he was and how incredible our experience was. We high-fived each other on another natural labor full of incredible teamwork. We stared at our little miracle and obsessed over his perfection as the midwife worked around us, doing her thing. My mom came upstairs with a glass of wine for her and brought Kyle a beer. We all hung out talking about the magic of this Universe Baby and his Mother's Day birthday!

I got up and had a shower while the midwives changed the sheets leaving fresh, clean ones on. That hot shower was so incredibly relaxing after the intense work of labor. I got into my big fluffy housecoat (not a drafty hospital gown), put on my own underwear (not those weird mesh undies) with a normal pad (not a huge blue pee sheet), slipped into my own bed (not a single mechanical cot) with my hubby beside me (not in the delivery room recliner) and had skin to skin with my newborn until we drifted off to sleep all together.

Pure ecstatic blissed-out magic. This was exactly the reason I wanted to have a home birth. Not once did we worry about when to leave for the hospital or when we were allowed to go home. Instead, we took our power back, made our own decisions, did things our own way, and hit another home run!

In the morning, my mom brought the boys upstairs to meet their new baby brother, and I was amazed at how they instantly adored him. That first family-of-five morning snuggle is a memory I will never forget. I loved to see that Rowan and Harvey were utterly unphased by the fact that I had their baby brother at home, in our bed, while they were sleeping. They never asked why I didn't go to the hospital or have any medicine. They thought it was the most normal thing in the world because it is!

The boys got to stay home from school and daycare that day so we could have a family day. We ordered breakfast, made smoothies and had a birthday party to welcome Baby Vance, complete with cake and gifts. It was a celebration on so many levels - welcoming a new family member, an easy straightforward home birth, and the accomplishment of a deeply desired personal life goal!

Hindsight is 20/20

As I reflect on my birth stories now, hindsight shows that each one had a distinct purpose in my life. It's a gift to have experienced the ups, and yes even the downs, of all these different births. They have made me a better teacher, and frankly, a better student. I am more accepting of the full breadth of life that comes my way; I'm more willing to look at experiences and find the lessons they're there to teach. I trust that even if something feels painful and I don't know its exact reason at the time, the greater purpose will be revealed later in life when looking back—in hindsight.

So although each of my births was better than the one before, I wouldn't change anything. I know that my home birth would not have been this profoundly meaningful to me—and Love Your Labour© wouldn't exist!—if I didn't have my previous two birth experiences. They were both an integral part of this beautiful bigger picture I get to look back on. And as an added bonus, thousands of women have had more empowered birth experiences because of them!

My wish for you is that you feel confident and empowered to absolutely rock your own birth. Fear can be overcome with education, and pain is manageable if you have the right tools. Tap into your inner birth goddess, and you'll see that birth is designed to be a beautifully divine, deliciously pleasurable experience for you and your partner to enjoy together in the privacy and comfort of your own home.

1. VBAC - Vaginal Birth After Cesarean
2. Meconium - the baby's first bowel movement is a black tarry substance called meconium, and when it is released into the amniotic fluid in labor, it can signify fetal distress.
3. Frank Breech - instead of the proper head-down position, the baby is in a bum-down position with their feet up by their ears.
4. Labor Funnel - the domino effect of unnecessary medical interventions in the hospital that makes achieving a natural birth significantly more difficult.
5. GBS - Group B Strep, which is a bacteria that they swab for in pregnancy, and if you test positive, it means you get antibiotics during your labour.
6. Intermittent Auscultation - the practice of doing a heart rate check every 15 minutes using the doppler to auscultate the baby's heart rate instead of external fetal monitoring.
7. Societal Birth Bias - the societal misconception that natural birth is terrifying, painful, and a problem that needs to be medicated away.
8. Durand, Mark A., MD, MPH. **"The Safety Of Home Birth: The Farm Study."** American Journal of Public Health, Vol 82, No.3 (March 1992): 450-453.

CORINNE BROWN

Corinne Brown is an author, former Naturopathic Doctor, mom of three, and CEO of her online business, Brownroots Love. Her mission is to help women become empowered to have positive birth experiences.

Corinne offers a free Natural Labour Prep Webinar for moms who are feeling nervous about natural birth. The webinar teaches strategies to dodge the Labor Funnel and achieve a positive, empowering experience.

With her online program, Love Your Labour©, Corinne gives step-by-step protocols that empower women to labor naturally and avoid unnecessary medical interventions. Natural birth is your birthright, and this program helps to stack the odds in your favour.

Because she knows that birth has the potential to be a deeply spiritual (even joyous and orgasmic!) experience, Corinne wants to make sure nothing stands in the way of that for you. She shares how to make your dream birth a fabulous reality inside her book, "The Badass Birth Goddess".

Corinne lives in Nova Scotia, Canada, and her other passions include meditation, spirituality, and yoga. She's also passionate about expressing herself through creating videos, dancing, playing the piano, and gardening. Corinne can often be found in the kitchen whipping up something yummy for her husband and three growing boys.

Website: www.brownroots.love
Email: hello@brownrootslove.com
Book: The Badass Birth Goddess
Instagram: @brownroots.love
Youtube: youtube.com/c/corinnebrownroots
Facebook:facebook.com/brownroots
LinkedIn: linkedin.com/in/corinnebrown-brownrootsinc/

5

PLAN B

HOME BIRTH TRANSFER TO HOSPITAL, FOLLOWED BY TWO
HOME BIRTH VBACS

ALISON SEDLAK

WHEN I FOUND out I was pregnant for the first time, there was no question in my mind that I would give birth naturally. My own mother delivered her five children in the hospital without any intervention; I could do the same. Of course, I was aware that complications *could* arise, but I didn't linger on those scenarios long. After all, I planned to deliver in a hospital, so I would have all the "backup" help I needed at a moment's notice.

I spent the first half of my pregnancy soaking up anything that had to do with birth and babies. I found an OB that was conveniently located near our apartment and beamed every time I got the report that my baby and I were in excellent health. I joined breastfeeding and cloth diapering support groups on Facebook. I arranged for my husband and me to attend private Bradley classes taught by a friend. I also devoured any and all reading material that promoted natural birth.

However, the more I read, the more I noticed a troubling theme. Hospitals didn't appear to be the best place to give birth naturally; their procedures actually seemed to hinder mothers from following their body's instincts. I saw plainly that every intervention increased the chances of delivering via c-section.

I started questioning if I was going to be prepared to fight for the birth I wanted when I was the one actually in labor. I didn't want to battle doctors and nurses about what was best for my body and my baby. I didn't want to be managed. I wanted to be trusted.

I realized that I needed a team that respected the labor process as I did. My husband fully supported my desire for a natural birth, but what if that wasn't enough? After all, this was his first time navigating a birth, too. I could start researching my local OB options with more scrutiny, but what if the doctor I chose wasn't working the day I went into labor?

I decided to ask my Bradley instructor friend if she would be my doula in the hospital. After all, she had also previously worked as a high-risk labor and delivery nurse. She would be prepared to advise me if I was thrown a curveball, right?

But as long as I was giving birth in a hospital, I knew I couldn't escape the policies that I would rather avoid. The very place that I used to trust as my "back up" now brought me more anxiety than peace. But what alternative did I have? I didn't feel ready to take on the risk and liability that came with giving birth at home.

What about a birth center?

Some of my reading material mentioned birth centers. I was intrigued by this third option. Was a birth center some kind of cross between a hospital and home setting? Could I find a place that set women up for successful natural labor while still offering them life-saving emergency services?

To my surprise, I found a birth center only twenty minutes from our apartment. Their website advertised monthly "birthing options" classes hosted at the center. I immediately wrote the next meeting on our calendar.

When I was 21 weeks pregnant, shortly after we found out we were having a boy, my husband and I found ourselves sitting in the homey birth center with several other curious couples. After a brief introduction, the owner had us all go around and share what brought us to the event that night. Many of the couples had already experienced a hospital birth that left them traumatized and wary of ever giving birth in a hospital again. I shared that I was looking for more control over my birth decisions but was feeling nervous about giving birth at home and wanted to know where birth centers fall on the spectrum of care.

The owner responded to my question by explaining that her birth center was no different from a home birth, medically speaking. If we wanted to have our baby at the birth center, we would have to pay a fee in order to use their facilities and independently hire a midwife. The midwife could also provide the same services in our home.

The midwives then introduced us to the laws that govern midwifery care, including the training, licensing, and experience required to attend a birth. I was highly impressed with their knowledge and professionalism that night. When they started sharing their philosophy of birth, I found myself giving my husband little approving glances. There are no rigid time limits for labor in a home birth or birth center. Laboring women are encouraged to move and try different labor positions and settings. Food and drink are regularly offered to fuel the marathon of the birth process. I felt a burden lifting off my shoulders the more they talked. This is what I was looking for.

Driving home, my husband and I agreed that home birth felt like the right choice for us! But now, we faced the task of hiring a midwife. After reading several introductions[1] on the birth center website, I contacted two midwives to set up interviews. I was 27 weeks pregnant when we sat down to meet the first one. A week later, we met the second. After weighing our options for a couple of days, we made our choice, and I set up my first appointment.

At six months pregnant, I found switching to midwifery care to be a deeply satisfying and grounding experience. My prenatal appointments, once a mere 15 minutes of time with my former OB, now lasted over an hour with my midwife. To say she provided holistic care is an understatement. She wanted to know details about my diet, sleeping patterns, emotional health, and support network that the OB never inquired about. She took the time to understand my concerns and questions about birth and to educate me about the changes happening in my body.

"And when do you expect to go into labor?" she once asked me. I replied that I always imagined going well past my due date because my mom was nearly two weeks "late" with all her kids. I couldn't believe that my midwife actually wrote my *hunch* down in her notes!

My favorite part of every visit was experiencing the magical touch of her expert hands as she gently explored my son's position within my expanding belly. Each time, after confirming that he was head down, she would paint a verbal picture of what he looked like inside me. The description always lined up perfectly with what I was feeling from the movements inside. My midwife created space for me; space to question, space to learn, and space to have the most incredible bonding experience with my son.

It's go time!

Just as I had suspected, my late August due date came and went with no signs of labor in sight. August turned into September, and I trusted that my son would come at the right time. Eleven days past my due date, the waiting game finally ended. My water broke around 9:00 pm. Like many first-time parents, we were revved up and ready for the "real thing" to be happening. My husband and I decided to go for a walk to try to get some contractions started. We called my midwife on our way out the door. She said that if the walking didn't work, we should just go to bed and try to rest before things started up on their own.

The walk didn't result in anything, so we reluctantly headed home. It was hard to unwind from my jittery anticipation, but I knew that it was wise to conserve my energy for the road ahead. My husband and I laid in bed, his arm draped over my belly as I laid on my side. My body relaxed, and I started to slip into a drowsy state. Suddenly, I felt my son move more forcefully and violently within me than he had ever moved before. "Woah!" I said to my husband. "Did you feel that? I felt him hit my pubic bone really hard. It was like he head-butted me from the inside!"

Within a few minutes, my contractions started. It was about 11:00 pm. We called my midwife to give her the update. "I'll come over whenever you want," she explained, "but you still have some time before I need to be there. I want to know when the contractions are coming in under five minutes apart." We decided to try laboring solo for a while.

I spent the next three hours in the comfort of my bed laboring and resting in between contractions. My husband started filling the birthing tub.

Around 2:00 am, my doula arrived. My contractions were around five minutes apart at that time, and then one came after three minutes. After getting our next call, my midwife arrived at about 2:20 am.

She observed me laboring for a few minutes and asked me how I was feeling. I told her that I was fine but that the contractions were ramping up. I asked her to check my dilation progress. As we prepared for the exam, we discovered that my pad was covered in a thick, dark, sticky substance.

"That's definitely meconium," my midwife said. She explained that the meconium was not mixed with any amniotic fluid, so his butt must be right at the opening of my cervix. My midwife examined me and informed me that I was about seven centimeters dilated. "And I definitely feel butt," she said with a serious look on her face. "Your son is breech."

Breech?! How could he be breech? He's been head down for two months! He must have flipped!

"Ok, you have a big decision to make here," my midwife continued. "I have been trained in how to deliver breech babies, but I've never actually delivered one. You can choose to stay here, but there are a lot of possible complications with a breech presentation that can quickly become quite serious. Otherwise, we need to transfer to the hospital, where you will likely have a c-section. I won't leave your side no matter what you choose."

We discussed our options. My husband fixated on turning our son to be head down. My midwife replied that she had turned breech babies before but never during active labor. All the while, I continued to experience contractions that were lengthening and getting more intense.

Then my doula asked me what I wanted.

What did I want? I wanted my beautiful natural water birth at home! I wanted to experience all the pain, the effort of pushing, the rush of oxytocin after my son was born. Was I ready to attempt a risky breech birth at home? Maybe it would all go well...or maybe we would find ourselves calling an ambulance.

What did I want? I wanted to meet my son. Losing him was unthinkable. I started to accept that this was no longer a low-risk pregnancy. I was no longer a good candidate for a home birth.

"It's time to go to the hospital," I finally replied. Without another word, everyone prepared to transfer. My midwife called ahead to let them know that we were coming and gathered the necessary paperwork they would want to see. My husband packed the bare necessities for a hospital stay. My doula stayed with me and coached me through contractions.

When it was time to leave, I walked out of the apartment with purpose. *I'm going to see my son.* I paced the building parking lot as my team packed the car. *I'm going to see my son.* I slowly lowered myself into the back seat of our car. *I'm going to see my son.*

And then we left.

The Hospital

Even though the car ride was only fifteen minutes long, it felt much longer. I remember trying to release tension from my body while simultaneously bracing myself through the stops and turns of a moving vehicle.

We pulled into the hospital parking lot around 3:30 am. Once in our room, the hospital staff immediately started hooking me up to the dreaded machines and asking me tons of questions. They confirmed that he was breech with a quick ultrasound scan. The fetal monitor showed that his heart rate was normal. A vaginal exam revealed that I was now fully dilated.

The doctor walked in, having been called from home. I can only imagine the thoughts going through her mind, knowing she was playing "home birth rescue" tonight.

I asked her if she would consider delivering a breech baby vaginally. She informed me that although she had delivered one breech in her career, a second twin, she would not be performing a vaginal breech delivery tonight. "If you want a natural labor," she said in a forceful tone, "you can get back in your car and drive to the next hospital."

My heart sank, but I replied, "I understand that I came here for a c-section. Thank you for accommodating us. We really appreciate the care."

Her demeanor changed immediately. "Taking care of you is my job, and that's exactly what we're going to do."

The room continued to buzz with conversation, and my contractions started to change. I was involuntarily starting to bear down. "Um, I hate to interrupt," I stammered, "but I really feel the urge to push."

I was immediately unhooked from the machines and rolled down the hall into an operating room. My husband was handed a set of scrubs and told to wait outside until the anesthesiologist had finished administering my spinal tap. *I'm going to see my son.*

Soon I was on my back, and my husband was admitted into the room. I felt a lot of pulling and tugging but no pain. *I'm going to see my son.*

All of a sudden, I felt my belly deflate like a balloon. A weight lifted off my body and spirit. I heard a cry and saw my son's little body lifted over the blue curtain for me to see, but only for a moment. They immediately carried him over to a warming center in my line of sight, where they began to clean him off. I begged my husband to follow.

My son stopped crying after he heard my husband's voice. My husband stood there and shielded our son's eyes from the bright lights above him. They both were so calm as my husband began to sing to him.

Soon enough, the doctors finished attending to my incision. I was ready to meet my son.

My husband carried him over to the operating table and held him tenderly over my shoulder. I looked into my baby's dark eyes for the first time and stroked his little forehead with my thumb. "Hi, baby," I murmured. "I'm your mommy. I've waited a long time to meet you, and we're so happy that you're finally here." I couldn't believe that I was actually looking at the beautiful life that I had carried for nine months.

Recovery

Within an hour of his birth, my son was nestled in my arms, skin to skin, latching for the first time. I found myself counting my blessings as I mentally adjusted to the fact that I was recovering in a hospital bed. My son was here. I carried him until I went into labor on my own. I labored for hours in the quiet of my own home. My cervix fully dilated before I got on the operating table. The surgical birth didn't seem to be impeding a healthy start to our breastfeeding relationship. The hospital staff respected my wishes for infant examinations to be done with my son in my arms.

I spent the next four days recovering in the hospital, constantly comparing my present circumstances with what my recovery *could* have been like at home. I let myself mourn the natural birth I lost. My plans for a home birth were unfulfilled, hanging in limbo. I needed to believe that my future births could be different. I decided to channel my grief into hope by setting my sights on a VBAC.

I started reading home birth VBAC stories on my phone from the hospital bed. I researched how to best recover from my c-section; I didn't want any physical complications to keep me from being able to labor naturally in the future. By the time we were discharged, I had already made a goal to wean off the pain medications by one week postpartum. I knew that I needed to feel when I was pushing myself too hard in order to heal well.

When my midwife came to our home for my six-week postpartum visit, we discussed the requirements for home birth VBACs in Wisconsin. I learned that we needed to have at least an 18-month break before our next baby. We also would need to have an overseeing OB confirm that the pregnancy was considered low-risk. In particular, I would need an ultrasound to make sure that the placenta was not attached to any c-section scar tissue.

I continued to have dull pain from the c-section for over six months. I avoided abdominal exercises altogether. The internal tugs I felt were a constant reminder to take it slow as I eased back into the physical tasks of daily life. By the time the cold Wisconsin winter had passed, our son was nine months old, and I felt more than ready to take daily walks. My body felt strong and restored. We enjoyed many trips to the playground that summer; I loved chasing after my active little boy.

Take Two

We celebrated our son's first birthday, and I started to daydream about my next pregnancy.

To my surprise, two weeks later, I discovered that I was already pregnant! I was thrilled to be expecting again but crestfallen at the thought of not being able to give birth at home because we hadn't been able to wait 18 months before we conceived again. I carried mixed emotions with me for two days before I had enough courage to call my midwife. I cried tears of relief when she explained that we needed 18 months between the c-section and the *birth* of the next baby! My VBAC could still happen at home!

After a whole year of studying VBAC, I entered my second pregnancy with a total commitment to achieving a vaginal birth. I was completely uncomfortable with more surgeries; the "risks" of a VBAC paled in comparison. The only thing that made me nervous was needing approval from a consulting OB. Luckily, I had heard of a local "home birth friendly" doctor from a few friends. I set up an appointment and hoped for the best.

I met with the doctor for the first time when I was 12 weeks pregnant. He listened attentively as I recounted the details of my son's birth, shared what I had researched about VBACs, and unveiled my hopes for pursuing a VBAC at home. "However," I explained, "It's most important to me that I am able to give birth vaginally, even if it had to be in a hospital. I'm simply not comfortable with the risks of a repeat c-section." I held my breath for what he would say.

He began by affirming what I had learned about VBACs and said that I was an excellent candidate for one. He complimented me on how informed my plans were. "You know, if I were a betting man," he remarked, "I'd put money down on your successful home birth VBAC."

I was speechless. He then asked me what role I wanted him to play in the pregnancy since I was also receiving prenatal care from my midwife. I told him that I wanted to see him every other month and that I would like his hospital to perform the twenty-week ultrasound, so they had easy access to my records in case I became high-risk again for any reason. "Done!" he replied.

I was practically pinching myself at that point. How was it possible that this member of the "mainstream medical establishment" was happily affirming my wishes for my baby and pregnancy?

Eight weeks later, and 20 weeks pregnant, I returned with my husband for another prenatal visit with the OB and the ultrasound. I was nervous. The stakes felt so high. Thankfully, the ultrasound revealed that my baby was healthy, and my placenta was nowhere near my scar. My home birth VBAC felt a lot closer that day.

At 28 weeks, I visited the doctor again. Our meeting, as always, was brief and completely respectful of my wishes.

At the same time, I continued to see my midwife every month until the third trimester, when I started seeing her every other week. Each visit confirmed that my blood pressure was excellent, weight gain was steady, urine samples were normal, and my belly size was measuring right on schedule. The baby was even consistently staying head down!

When I reached 36 weeks, my midwife called my overseeing OB to have the "consultation" required for her to oversee my labor at home. At our next appointment, she reported the good news that he officially considered me an excellent candidate for a VBAC.

I saw the doctor one last time at 39 weeks. Unless I developed complications or reached 42 weeks, I wouldn't need to see him again. We scheduled a non-stress test the day before 42 weeks, just in case.

Waiting

Again, my due date came and went. While I wasn't personally worried about being "overdue," I was acutely aware that my midwife's license only allowed her to deliver babies between 37 and 42 weeks. If I reached the end of that range, I would be left with hoping for a VBAC in the hospital, where they would likely insist upon an induction. I knew that a hospital induction actually decreased my chances of having a successful VBAC.

Once I reached 41 weeks, I was ready to give my baby a nudge. I decided to schedule an appointment with a friend who is an acupuncturist. It was a totally new experience; there were needles in my lower back, ear, hand, ankle, and on the outside corner of my pinky toe, all in an effort to stimulate my uterus and cervix. Two days later, I went back for a second session. It didn't seem to be making a difference, but my acupuncturist friend assured me that it was priming my body for labor.

Then my doula asked me if I had looked into taking castor oil. After a quick google search, I learned that castor oil is a laxative that not only empties the bowels but can irritate the uterus, stimulating contractions. I read several birth stories in which women claimed that castor oil successfully jumpstarted their labors. But a lot of them also reported the castor oil making them sick. I was totally uninterested in experiencing vomiting or diarrhea while laboring.

Yet, the 42-week mark was only four days away. Castor oil started looking like a viable option. I asked my midwife if she had any experience with clients using castor oil. She said that she did and that she had a specific protocol to follow for the best results.

I agonized over trying castor oil as another day of waiting passed by. I messaged my acupuncturist friend to see if she had any stories to share. She replied that castor oil had worked for her sister but that it had definitely made her sick. Now that she was aware that I was still pregnant, she volunteered to help me with my labor in any way she could, reminding me that she had supported many VBAC clients with acupuncture during labor. I was touched by her offer.

With only two days until I hit 42 weeks, I resolved to try a castor oil smoothie the next morning if I didn't go into labor that night. My doula would come over to keep me company and monitor whether it seemed to be working or not.

The next day, I made the smoothie an hour after having a good breakfast. It proved to be way too much for my stomach, and I threw everything up within an hour. Not knowing how much castor oil I may have digested, I kept following my midwife's protocol and hooked myself up to a breast pump.

The pump did stimulate some mild contractions. However, every time I went off the machine, they died off completely. I went back on the pump a few times that day, always encouraged when the contractions started up again. My doula and I decided to take a walk, hoping to ramp up the intensity of the contractions, but with no success.

As we headed back to the apartment, I was holding back tears. *I only have two days to give birth at home. Why does forty-two weeks have to be this magical cut-off date? I just need more time!*

I went to bed that night, defeated and exhausted.

The next day was the scheduled non-stress test with my overseeing OB. I was so nervous about what the test might mean for me, but, thankfully, my baby passed the test with flying colors. "I thought I wasn't supposed to see you folks again!" my consulting doctor said with a wink. "I guess your baby is pretty comfortable in there, huh?"

Looking ahead, the doctor agreed that there was no reason to induce simply because I had reached the 42-week mark. However, he did report that the probability of unexplained stillbirth rises exponentially between 42 and 43 weeks and that he wasn't comfortable letting the pregnancy continue more than a few days past 42 weeks. We agreed to schedule a gentle hospital induction at 42 weeks and two days.

The doctor noticed how nervous I looked when discussing the induction. "I am committed to helping you get your VBAC," he assured me. "That means I won't be giving you any kind of timeline for your labor as long as you and the baby continue to be in good shape. I want you to have all the time you need for your VBAC."

My heart was heavy, but I was grateful. I knew that not every doctor would be this understanding and supportive. At the same time, the more I thought about the possibility of another hospital birth, the more resolved I became to have this baby before that could happen.

On the drive home, I texted my midwife and doula to share the good results of the non-stress test. I also told them that I would be taking a shot of castor oil as soon as I got home. It was time to get this baby out.

Eviction Time

We arrived home around 3:00 pm. This time, I mixed four ounces of castor oil with just two ounces of orange juice. Within an hour, I took my first trip to the toilet. The digestive effects of the castor oil appeared to be working this time, without making me feel sick. All the toilet stops that followed simply cleared out my system. This I didn't mind since the only thing I wanted to push out in that birth tub later was a baby.

I took a short nap and woke up around 4:30 to some mild contractions. I texted my midwife to give her an update and then tried to rest and conserve my energy in case this was really the beginning of labor.

My contractions continued on their own, but remained incredibly easy. My midwife stopped by around 6:30. I asked her to check my dilation. She determined that I was about four centimeters. Hours of painless labor followed, and no movement or position had any effect on the frequency, intensity, or duration of the contractions. By midnight, I was desperate. I knew that I needed something to push my body over the edge.

I called my acupuncturist friend and asked her if it would be possible for her to come immediately. She said that she would come right over.

She arrived at our apartment around 1:00 am. We headed straight to the bedroom to try another round of acupuncture. I reclined on my side and propped several pillows around me to support myself.

First, she put two small needles in my hand. Then she added one to my ear. The next needles were placed in my calves and ankles. Finally, she inserted the last needle on the outside edge of my right pinky toe, a uterine point. Immediately after the needle pricked my toe, I felt a gush.

"My water just broke."

"Oh, that was fast...do you want me to continue?"

"Go get my midwife."

She left, and I experienced my first real contraction. It took considerable effort to keep myself from tensing up. I knew at that moment that I had crossed a threshold.

My midwife rushed into the room with a fetal monitor to check the baby's heartbeat. My husband looked on with a new spark in his eyes.

It was about 1:30. I decided to keep the needles inserted for as long as I could manage. It grew harder and harder to lie motionless with every passing contraction. Eventually, I asked my acupuncturist friend to remove the needles; I simply had to get up and move around.

Soon, I was pacing the living room, leaning over the couch as contractions came. They were getting harder to deal with on my own.

By 2:30, I was begging my midwife to tell me when it would all be over. She gently suggested that I try the birth tub. I debated whether or not to get in. I knew that I wanted to save the tub for the very end. After a few more contractions, I announced that I was getting in the tub. It was 2:50.

As I slipped into the warm water, I felt my body relax. But that moment of peace passed as soon as the next contraction came on. I don't know what I expected the water to do to the labor pains, but it didn't seem to do anything!

The new sensation of weightlessness helped me try several different laboring positions without much effort. It wasn't long before I was feeling the urge to push.

This part of the labor was new for me. I never knew how hard a woman has to push in order to get a baby out! I was pushing with everything I had. Time seemed to disappear.

Instinctually, I reached down to feel for my baby. I felt a head! I continued to push, now with my fingertips connected to my prize. I was addicted to the touch of my little one. I felt the baby's progress with every effort I gave.

I felt the head come out. My midwife positioned my husband's hands to catch the baby. With the next push, the body slipped out. My midwife coached my husband to keep the baby under the water while she freed a tiny foot from an umbilical cord tangle. Then she guided his hands to transfer the baby to me. Once the head emerged from the warm water into the cool air, the baby let out a cry. I lifted a leg to discover that we had a daughter.

"It's a girl!" I announced. "Hello, my girl! I'm your mama! You're finally here!"

The aftermath of our home birth was a welcome change from our hospital recovery. I was immediately offered food and drink from my own kitchen. I rested in my own bed, wrapped in soft towels and blankets. My toddler son was still asleep, just a room away, unaware that he was now a big brother.

Some people are shocked when they find out that I gave birth at home after experiencing a "home birth gone wrong." My transfer to the hospital was not a "failed plan A," but a "successful plan B." I knew that home birth was no longer a wise option once I found out my son was breech. The hospital provided services that were an appropriate fit for my unforeseen circumstances. And I am so grateful for the care they gave me.

What I longed for as a pregnant woman was agency. I wanted to be able to make informed choices for my body and my baby, and I did! I made the final call to transfer. Getting to make that decision myself played a huge role in grieving and healing emotionally after my hospital birth.

But I know that pregnancy is not a disease. Pregnancy is a normal function of a healthy female body. As long as a woman and her baby are well and the pregnancy is low-risk, midwives are more than capable of providing quality prenatal and postpartum care.

Finally achieving my VBAC brought closure to my heart and body. Natural labor is truly an amazing, life-changing experience. Living through both a hospital and a home birth helped me to respect the uncertainty of life's best-made plans while also teaching me to hold on to hope.

---

1. http://well-roundedmaternity.com/directory

ALISON SEDLAK

Alison Sedlak has a teaching degree from the University of Wisconsin-Madison and is certified to teach first through eighth grade. She taught third grade in Milwaukee, WI, for several years before leaving the classroom to raise and homeschool her three children. She chose to pursue a home birth during the third trimester of her first pregnancy, only to need a hospital transfer when the baby was unexpectedly found in a breech position. She chooses to label her c-section a "successful plan B." Thankfully, she was able to have two successful home birth VBACs with her following pregnancies. She loves mentoring young moms who are willing to challenge mainstream approaches to parenting, whether they are navigating birth or educational choices. When she isn't teaching her children or tutoring others in math, you can find her escaping to the backyard to take care of her "fourth child," her vegetable garden.

Email: planBbirthstory@gmail.com

6

A CERTIFIED NURSE MIDWIFE'S PERSPECTIVE

FROM HOME TO HOSPITAL TO HOME

PAULA FADWAH HALABY

Background

I HAVE ALWAYS BEEN a die-hard home birth advocate after birthing all six of my biological children at home. The first in 1985 was with just my partner by my side in a hippie house in Arcata, CA—before 'free-birth' was a term that people used. I did have some help from actual lay midwives for four of the births, with another unassisted birth with baby number three. Fast forward to 2006, nine years after my last home birth, and a year after completing my training as a Certified Nurse Midwife (CNM), I began working for a busy OB/GYN (Obstetrics/Gynecology) doctor group as their first CNM employee. In eight years, I assisted over 1600 women to birth in the hospital—with and without epidurals or IV (intravenous) pain meds, on their sides, backs, and hands and knees. Some were unmedicated because that was their choice, some because there was no time for drugs, and many of them with Pitocin (synthetic oxytocin that makes contractions stronger and more regular) because that's how it's done in the hospital. It's a rare hospital birth that doesn't have the addition of Pitocin to the mix. Think of the hospital L&D (Labor and Delivery) unit as a pressure cooker: as women filter in through the triage area, scheduled and unscheduled, the unit fills up, and within 1-2 hours of giving birth, they filter back out to the postpartum area. So the longer they are there laboring, the longer that bed is taken and can't be used until they're done and gone. Lack of efficiency leads to babies being born in triage or scheduled inductions told to wait at home. Also, it just isn't profitable to 'allow' women to labor naturally, as this doesn't result in the birth of a baby in the timeframe that gets the most dollars for the use of the space.

My job also required me to work as a member of a team of doctors and midwives. We all took turns staffing our three offices (four OB doctors and five CNMs) and covering the 'floor' as we called it—the L&D units of two hospitals. We each had a hospital day every week where we took care of laboring moms and performing surgery for scheduled and unscheduled cesareans—the doctors performed the surgery, and the midwife would assist. There were rounds to do—checking in with laboring or postpartum moms, and the best part of all—catching babies!

I spent countless hours in the hospital and became intimately familiar with everything that went on in the areas of L&D and the postpartum unit. It was easy to see that although some women came through relatively unscathed, others were traumatized to some degree. It was a roll of the dice because it had a lot to do with who was on call when you happened to show up. The decisions made by a provider in the early hours of an induction, for instance, could influence whether or not that induction ended in a vaginal or cesarean birth. And our group was similar to all the other large groups in that we followed a call schedule which prevented us from being able to be available for a particular person at a random time. Some OBs are solo providers or in two or three person groups, which makes it more predictable for the client. But unless that provider is on the same page as the birthing person, the risk of unexpected interventions is always there. The alternative is to schedule an induction, but then you aren't having a truly natural birth.

For four days every week, I was in the office. I saw over 500 women every month for GYN and pregnancy related visits. I loved my job—I loved meeting people, talking about women's bodies, and helping to make them feel better when they had an infection or other problem. I tended to suggest natural remedies whenever I could, and I found that clients gravitated to me. My schedule was always full, and many women asked for me and wouldn't see anyone else if they could help it. I was personable and kind and treated them with respect—always asking permission to touch them and using the gentlest touch I could while still being effective with whatever I was doing. I carried this attitude into the hospital and found myself at odds with the nursing staff, who seemed always to be in a hurry. I really don't blame the nurses, but rather the culture of birth in the hospital where the nurses are understaffed, underpaid, and overworked.

Eventually, the midwife that I was at heart could no longer bear to participate in the crass culture of childbirth in the hospital. My body began to break down. I developed a frozen shoulder and realized that I had to slow down and get away from the toxicity of hospital birth. I think the most painful, traumatizing part was watching the way the babies are handled. I remembered how my own babies slipped into the world into my loving hands or those of a trusted friend or midwife and then immediately put them to my chest. We would talk lovingly and softly to them and watch them unfold like a flower in their first moments of breathing air. Often their eyes would be open as they immediately began exploring this strange new world. And they all began breathing without any help. In contrast, in a hospital birth, as soon as the baby is out (sometimes before the body is born), a bulb syringe is forcefully thrust into the back of the baby's throat (to suction normal secretions), the baby is flopped onto mom's stomach, the cord is immediately cut, and then the baby is roughly rubbed down with a flannel blanket until s/he begins screaming. The parents are told that it's good for the baby to scream when they try to stop the rubbing. It was heartbreaking—birth after birth after birth.

From Hospital to Home

I decided that I needed to quit my job. I couldn't stomach watching the way the babies were handled, and I decided that I couldn't save women from the choice they had made to have their baby in the hospital. I tried to protect everyone that I had the fortune to cross paths with, and I believe that contributed to my health problems. So I decided I would open my own practice and offer an alternative. There were plenty of Licensed Midwives (LM) in the area offering home birth, but no Certified Nurse Midwives. My colleagues all practiced in the hospital. To this day, only about 15.8% of CNMs offer out-of-hospital services, and most of them are in Birth Centers. What I really wanted to do was open a Birth Center, offer home birth and also have hospital privileges so that I could care for those who were afraid to birth outside the hospital. The other benefit of hospital privileges is to be able to transfer to the hospital with a home or Birth Center client when transfer becomes necessary.

What I discovered is that it is nearly impossible to find an OB willing to back up a CNM doing home birth. And none who truly support a home birth CNM to have hospital privileges. So I have focused on home birth for the past seven years. Midwife360 has assisted over 300 home births—VBAC (after 1, 2, 3, even 4 previous cesareans!), twins, breeches, older moms, younger moms, Black, Hispanic, White, Asian, big women, little women, early babies, late babies, big babies, little babies – we have been privileged to experience it all!

What Does It Look Like?

Home is a safe space, a personal space where the exact location of the birthing tub has been decided on with input from the midwife at the

36 week home visit. All of the supplies that the family is asked to provide are neatly placed in proximity to the intended place of birth; things like towels, receiving blankets for the baby, paper towels, and trash bags. We typically recommend the couples' bedroom, but sometimes another spot is chosen for various reasons. This might be the baby's room, a guest bedroom, a corner of the living room, a big bathroom, even the kitchen! There is dim lighting, sometimes candles, or Christmas lights. She may have birth affirmations hanging on the walls. Hypnosis for labor and birth may be playing on a Bluetooth device or on headphones or earbuds that only the mother can hear. Alternatively, there is meditative music playing softly in the background. Other children are either asleep or being tended to by another adult so the father of the baby (or birthing person's partner) can be attending to the needs of the laboring mom. She is alone, focused on allowing her body to do the work of bringing her baby. The less distraction, the more she is able to open and release any fear or tension she may be holding on to. Her doula is attending to the couple, encouraging the partner with comfort measures, and helping the labor progress by suggesting activities or positions that facilitate the movement of the baby through the woman's body.

When the time is right, as evidenced by the contraction pattern and the behavior of the birthing person, the doula facilitates getting the tub set up and filled, and the midwife is called. When the midwife arrives, she assesses the labor by watching and listening to the birthing mother and perhaps checking her cervix to determine her dilation. This is not always necessary as the progress of labor can be determined solely by the contraction pattern and behavior of the mom. The midwife will begin monitoring—listening to FHT (fetal heart tones) every half hour, taking the mom's blood pressure (every hour) and temperature (every four hours unless her waters have released, then it's every hour). If the mom is GBS (group beta strep) positive, IV antibiotic prophylaxis will be offered and begun if desired. The birth supplies are set up by the midwife, and the waiting is begun. Ideally, the midwife is called two to four hours prior to the birth of the baby. It rarely happens like that, though. It's either much longer or almost right before the baby arrives! I've midwifed many women over the phone while I was rushing to get there—too many couples are afraid to get us there too soon! Also, when laboring at home, labor tends to be not as painful as they remember from their hospital experience, so they wait too long to call because they don't think they are as far into their labor as they actually are.

We bring everything to a home birth that would be found in a Birth Center or Level 1 hospital. We have O2 (oxygen) and an ambu bag (for ventilating the baby if necessary), IV supplies with fluids and antibiotics, other drugs such as Pitocin, Methergine, and Cytotec (all for postpartum hemorrhage), Zofran (for nausea), and Lidocaine (for perineal repair, if necessary). We carry sterile instruments to cut the baby's cord or suture the mom. Many midwives also use alternative therapies like a TENS unit (transcutaneous electrical nerve stimulation) for pain relief and homeopathics, essential oils, and herbs to help encourage contractions or calm the mother's fears or tension when needed. The birthing tub has been referred to as 'a liquid epidural', and that's really the crown jewel of home birth. There are few hospital programs that 'allow' laboring in the water and even fewer that 'allow' water birth. (In the United States, that is. There are lots of hospital programs doing water birth abroad in countries such as India, Dubai, China, and many others thanks to the work of Barbara Harper, LM/RN)

When the time is right, the laboring mom gets into the tub—the relaxation and relief are audible and visible as she emits a huge sigh and sinks down into the warm water. And when her body is ready, she begins to push. It typically starts with a catch in her breath and within a little while will become outright pushing efforts. At home, pushing is almost never coached as the body does this naturally when the baby gets low enough in the birth canal. It is rarely necessary to do a cervical exam at this point as the baby begins to move down.

Before long, we can start to see something visible at the opening of the vagina. If mom is on her knees leaning over the side of the tub, we use a mirror and underwater flashlight to help us watch more and more of the presenting part to show. This is when we will urge the mom to try to breathe through her contractions, easing the baby's head over the perineum. We encourage her to touch her baby's head and get a sense of how swiftly she is bringing him/her out. The slower this part goes, the less chance there is of the vagina tearing.

With a last easy push, the head clears the perineum, and there is palpable relief from the mom. We watch as the baby slowly turns to allow the shoulders to pass through the pelvic bones and slip out. This can happen right away or with the next contraction that could be five minutes later. The baby will not try to breathe until his/her face is out of the water. The first breath is triggered by the trigeminal nerve being exposed to the air. Babies are floating in the amniotic fluid when they're in the womb and making breathing movements throughout the last trimester of pregnancy. Their lungs are filled with lung fluid. When they are born into water, they still have that fluid in their lungs. It's not until they are taken out of the water that they spit, cough, and swallow that fluid in order to make room for air to go in.

Most babies have their eyes open at this point because the light is not bright. They are curious to see where they are and to meet their mom for the first time, face to face. They go right into 'the sanctuary'— between the mother's breasts—right on the other side of the space they occupied for the past nine months. They feel safe, and they begin to explore their world with their hands and their mouths. This is the critical seeding of their microbiome, which will support their immune system. These babies don't scream. They may cry a little— just enough to help clear their lung fluid—and then they are quietly taking in their world. Within two hours, their lungs are clear, and they have successfully transitioned into our world.

At this point, it's all about making sure both mom and baby continue to transition safely. We are monitoring the baby's temperature, heart and respiratory rate, and mom's blood pressure and bleeding. The placenta is birthed usually within an hour, and the cord is cut once it becomes flaccid and white, also typically about an hour after birth. Breastfeeding is initiated within the first hour, usually while waiting for the placenta. Once the placenta is birthed, the baby can be handed to the dad (skin to skin on his chest and covered with a blanket—this keeps the baby warm), and mom is helped out of the tub. Sometimes she goes to the bed where her perineum is examined for tears and sutured if necessary, or sometimes straight to the shower where she is encouraged to pee and rinse off, and then brought to the bed for perineal repair if needed, and the shower happens after. She is fed a warm meal while the baby is examined head to toe for any abnormalities. We sprinkle goldenseal powder on the cord stump (for its antibacterial and drying properties). Then we measure and weigh the baby and apply coconut or olive oil liberally to the diaper area (to make it easier to wipe off the baby's first poops) before putting on the first diaper. After that, we tuck the family into bed. Interspersed with all of the care of mom and baby, the birth team is emptying the tub, sanitizing all of the equipment, and putting things away bit by bit. It always feels a little bit like The Cat in The Hat with Thing One and Thing Two the way we swoop in, make a big mess, and then clean it all up and pack it out!

The Culture of Birth

The culture of birth in America—and in many developed countries around the world—is not what most consumers are looking for. This is evidenced by many women having a baby in the hospital and then switching to home or birth center the next time around. In the Listening to Mothers III survey, mothers were asked about settings where they might be interested in giving birth in the future. Among those planning more children, two-thirds would consider a birthing center that is separate from a hospital, with one-fourth definitely wanting that option. A little more than one-fourth would consider a home birth. That does not speak very highly of customer satisfaction for hospital birth in general. One reason for this is that physiologic birth is not supported in the hospital setting very well. While it is possible to achieve a natural birth in the hospital, it is difficult. In contrast, at home or in a birth center, it is much easier to have the ambiance that supports physiologic birth. For a healthy, relatively low-risk pregnancy, the high-tech atmosphere in the hospital is simply not necessary. From my experience taking care of hundreds of women who have chosen to birth at home after having one or more hospital births, the lure of the epidural just isn't enough to bring them back to the hospital. Another reason is the lack of autonomy women experience at the hospital. As soon as they arrive, they are stripped of their clothes, put into a hospital gown, hooked up to the monitor, and tied to an IV pole for a continuous IV infusion. They are prohibited from eating or drinking—given only ice chips and made to stay in the bed. None of these are evidence-based practices. The lights are bright, and there are strangers coming in and out of the room randomly for signatures or lab work. It is no wonder that labor progresses slowly, and over two-thirds of women will ask for an epidural. Cervical checks are performed every two hours, membranes are "stripped", amniotic sacs are ruptured, Pitocin is administered, episiotomies are performed, and cords are immediately cut – all without asking permission. These practices are chasing women away from hospital birth care.

Choosing a Provider

Most home birth providers are midwives who are not nurses. Some of them are Certified Professional Midwives (CPM), although some choose not to become certified, and some may also be nurses, but are not the same as Certified Nurse Midwives (CNM). Some home birth midwives are licensed by their state, and some states still consider this type of midwifery to be illegal, while a few states don't license midwives but also don't have laws against them. CNMs are legal in every state, while some states prohibit them from providing home birth services. Birth Centers are legal in every state and can have MDs, CNMs, or CPMs working in them. When choosing an out-of-hospital provider, it is very important to do your research. Look for reviews and consider the number of reviews as well as the content. Ask around and join the local natural mamas FaceBook groups. Interview several before settling on the one you like. Some important questions to ask would be:

What is your transfer rate?
What kinds of things do you transfer for?
What would cause me to risk out of your care?
How many births have you attended as the primary midwife?
How do you feel about alternative therapies?
Do you recommend that I have a doula?
How many clients do you take on at a time?
What happens if you have two clients in labor at the same time?

It is important that you find someone who trusts birth and women's bodies; someone who is courageous but not reckless. You have to try to establish whether or not you are on the same page about the things that are important to you, so doing your homework ahead of time by considering and listing those things would be helpful. Some folks choose their doula first and then consider her recommendations when finding their provider. Many doulas have worked with a lot of different providers and have seen them in action under different circumstances and so have a good idea about how they react under stress. Does the provider treat you with respect? Listen to your questions and take the time to answer them thoughtfully? A good provider will incorporate a lot of education into the care that they provide. How long are the prenatal visits? At the end of the day, it is your body, your birth, your baby, so your wishes and desires are paramount, and this should be reflected in the way you are treated by your provider.

What's Wrong With the System?

The American College of Obstetricians and Gynecologists (ACOG) has a document describing their position on planned home birth. It is The ACOG Committee Opinion on Planned Home Birth which was authored in 2011 and reaffirmed in 2015. The main points are that although they state that they believe the hospital to be the safest place to have a baby, they agree with a woman's right to choose where and with whom to give birth. They also recommend the appropriate selection of clients for home birth and that home birth is safest with a CNM, Certified Midwife (CM), or physician 'practicing within an integrated and regulated health system; ready access to consultation; and assurance of safe and timely transport to nearby hospitals." They see these factors as "critical to reducing perinatal mortality rates and achieving favorable home birth outcomes." So even while the OB doctors' national college recommends an integrated system, lack of integration has been the biggest obstacle consistently experienced across the system by home birth providers. Most hospital birth workers—the obstetricians and nurses who care for birthing people in the hospital systems—view home birth midwives with cynical skepticism as untrained, inexperienced, reckless, and even downright dangerous. The reason for this is that what they see are the transfers. These clients, who either have risked out of home birth for one reason or another, who have been unable to achieve the birth at home before becoming completely exhausted and unable to tolerate the pain any longer, or who are actually experiencing an emergency complication. Most clients who choose birth at home want their provider to try everything possible to achieve a successful birth as long as mom and baby are tolerating the situation well. We allow labor way more time than they are accustomed to doing in the hospital environment. So they perceive any transfers as 'train wrecks' requiring them to clean up our messes. When in actuality, what is happening is a transfer to a higher level of care, much as would happen when a patient is moved from a regular medical unit into the

ICU when their condition deteriorates. The ICU doesn't blame the other unit; they accept the client and move on. This doesn't happen with home birth transfers; midwives are judged, and clients are punished. It is completely unacceptable but not an easy problem to fix. If there was a way to allow the hospital personnel to witness the successful, beautiful, satisfying birth experiences that don't transfer, then they might have a different attitude. There are rare cases of malpractice by home birth providers, but this occurs in the hospital as well, and probably a lot more often than it occurs at home.

The Ideal System

One solution would be to create a registry system of midwives with every hospital. Midwives would determine the hospitals that are in proximity to their clients' homes and sign up on the registry. The hospitals could confirm that they are trained and licensed. Then when a client goes into labor, the midwife would alert the hospital that they have a labor in progress and send the client's records over so that the doctor on call could review them. This way, if the midwife needs to consult or transfer the client, there would be an easily accessed resource for them. The nurses on duty would know there was a chance that this client might be coming in. Once the birth is over, another call could be placed to let them know that the baby was born and everyone was good. We are all on the same page, after all, with safety for the mother and baby as the paramount concern. We could work together to ensure this outcome while at the same time supporting those who choose to birth in the comfort and familiarity of their own home. This is the task of our generation in regards to the culture of childbirth in America.

Bringing it Home

Just after our country went into full pandemic mode, in June of 2020, I was fortunate to have a lull in my practice and a midwife willing to hold down the fort for me while I traveled to Colorado to assist in the home birth of my youngest grandchild. My daughter had had her first baby in the hospital and the second in a birth center, both with CNM care. For this pregnancy, she had been getting standard care with an OB and CNMs who assist women in the hospital, but she did not want to go to the hospital for her birth. Once the hospital L&D units began shifting their policies regarding visitors and stopped allowing doulas or extra family members to participate in birth due to COVID19, women were leaving their hospital plans in droves. Every home birth midwife practice was suddenly filled to capacity, and they had to turn people away. Some folks decided to birth unassisted. My daughter was lucky that I had made my plans ahead of time and was able to travel to be with her and her family. After three and a half weeks of waiting and a 17 hour labor, we had the most beautiful, loving, family-centered water birth in her basement. She was surrounded by her partner, her two little daughters, her mom, and all of her sisters. I felt so much gratitude for being there for her both as her midwife and as her mother. While every home birth I attend is filled with love, this one was even more special as I got to shower all that love on my own family while also using my skills as a midwife. There is no better way to welcome our most precious resource—the next generation—than a gentle birth at home.

PAULA FADWAH HALABY

Fadwah has given birth six times at home and raised five more children over the years through her rich blended family experiences. She has lived in the mountains of Colorado and also enjoys the sunny lifestyle of South Florida. She is a Nurse Practitioner with a specialty in Midwifery (CNM). She has a BS with an emphasis in Nutrition from The Evergreen State College in Olympia, WA. In the 1980s and 90s, she studied childbirth education and then received homebirth training in Colorado. Her certificate in Nurse-Midwifery is from Frontier School of Midwifery and Family Nursing, 2005 (now Frontier Nursing University).

Along the way, she worked in several Emergency Rooms and Labor and Delivery units. Once she completed midwifery school, she worked for a very busy, local OB/GYN group of five midwives and four MDs. She assisted over 1600 women in giving birth at two hospitals in Palm Beach County and frequently saw over 500 women in the office every month. It is her intimacy with the medical model of care that makes her such a great choice for birth at home. She is confident that when supported in a physiologic manner, pregnant people will birth gracefully, with freedom into the loving embrace of their families.

Website: https://midwife360.com/
Email: fadwah@midwife360.com
Facebook: https://www.facebook.com/midwife360/
Instagram: https://www.instagram.com/midwife360/

7

FREEDOM TO MOVE AT HOME

A PHYSICAL THERAPIST'S HOSPITAL BIRTH AND SUBSEQUENT HOME BIRTHS

DR. AMANDA CLEARY PICKART PT, DPT

I DID NOT THINK about my first labor and delivery experience for many months. In part because my partner, Jason, and I experienced a steep learning curve in becoming parents. Breastfeeding was hard, my nipples were inverted, and I fumbled with a nipple shield for much of the early days. Our baby, Finn, could not lie on his back without screaming, diaper changes were a nightmare, he would not sleep in a crib, and we did not know it was possible to bedshare safely. The first six weeks, Jason stayed up all night so Finn could sleep upright on his chest and would bring him to me when he was hungry and then slept during the day. We were like watchmen on opposite shifts, only briefly seeing each other during shift changes. We spent our days bouncing for hours on the exercise ball and sitting perfectly upright with a baby on our chest.

Our pediatrician told us we just had a colicky baby and suggested we prop the crib mattress at an angle. I asked how that would work since the mattress angle would have to be set at 90 degrees. Maybe I should try duct-taping my baby to the bed? Eventually, it was suggested to try a probiotic. We also discovered the research by James McKenna and learned how to bedshare safely. With time, the probiotic, and the works of James McKenna, I finally got to see and enjoy my baby for the bright-eyed, happy little one he is.

While my oldest, Finn, was born in the hospital, I chose a different path for my two younger children, Rowan and Sage. I chose home. I guess you could say once I experienced what birth could be like at home, I was hooked.

The road to choosing home birth was a winding one. If you asked me how my birth went in the immediate days after Finn was born, I would tell you it was perfect. That oxytocin is a powerful hormone. Baby and I were both healthy, so that is all that matters, right? That phrase makes me cringe now, but it is such a prevalent saying, I had internalized that idea and believed it.

As Finn grew older, the thoughts of adding a sibling started to creep in, and with that, the thoughts of choosing a healthcare provider. I had heard the advice of choosing the right healthcare provider is one of the most important decisions you will make during your pregnancy journey. I personally value more naturally inclined options and believe strongly in the power of the body. It is partly why I became a physical therapist so I could teach others how to heal through movement. When I was deciding which provider to work with, I wanted someone that would support my wish to birth without interventions. I wanted a midwife.

Unfortunately, when I was pregnant with Finn, we were living in an area with few birth resources and no midwives. Instead, I selected a doctor whose biography included words such as "preventative care" and "minimally invasive surgery." I figured this was as close as I was going to get to the mindset I was seeking.

When I had the opportunity to start searching for a healthcare provider for our second pregnancy, we were in the process of moving to Madison, WI, which is a city rich in resources related to the birthing community. I knew I wanted to work with a midwife, and in my first online search, I was instantly given the opportunity to decide between a hospital-based midwife and a home-based midwife. I did not know home was an option until then, and I wanted to learn more.

As I started to consider what a home birth could look like, I also started to reflect on my first labor and delivery experience and realized there were several moments that I felt my voice was not heard. The most pivotal moment I wish I could change was the discussion that happened at my 40-week appointment.

Finn's Hospital Birth Story

At this 40-week appointment, we went through all the standard tests and assessments. Little Finn got glowing reviews, and I was thinking, "wonderful, see you next week." I assumed I would go past my guess date[1] since I was a first-time mom, and also, my mom often tells me stories of how long she waited for me to arrive. Instead, my doctor said for the first time, "I don't let my moms go past 41 weeks because the research shows the risk of stillbirth increases, so how do you feel about being induced tonight?" I was stunned. I did not want to cause harm to my baby. I asked about what induction looked like. She talked about the difference between Pitocin[2] and Cervidil[3]. She did not tell me her protocol for induction was continuous fetal monitoring[4], that I would not be able to move around the room or even the bed. I wish I had asked her protocol for monitoring post-term babies earlier in my pregnancy. I wish I had asked the rate of stillbirth at different gestational ages. I wish I had asked for time to think and discuss the options with my partner. I was told to go home, have a nice dinner, and check into the hospital around 9 pm. My doctor said the nurses at the hospital already knew she would likely be sending a mom their way tonight. It seemed everyone knew I was going to have a baby tonight, except me.

The excitement of finally getting to meet Finn took over after that appointment. Jason and I had a nice dinner, packed our hospital bag, and headed the 16 miles to the nearest hospital along a very bumpy road. I was at that moment thankful not to be in labor driving along this road. We checked in. I opted for Cervidil. I had heard too many stories of Pitocin being used to the point that your body could not cope, so an epidural is needed, but the side effects of the epidural can cause labor to slow down, so the two interventions create this competing effect. In some ways, I am not sure it really mattered which medical induction technique I chose. Either way, it is an invitation for a cascade of interventions—exactly what I was hoping to avoid.

The Cervidil started, as did an IV to keep me hydrated, an antibiotic because I was group beta strep (GBS) positive, and a belt was strapped to me for continuous external fetal monitoring. I could not move in bed because every time I moved, it caused an error, and they would lose track of Finn's heartbeat. The Cervidil did eventually make Finn tachycardic[5], so that was removed, but the contractions continued. The next morning my doctor was concerned the contractions were not strong enough, so she recommended artificial rupture of the membrane. I did not feel like I had a choice. I knew the waves[6] needed to be stronger to bring Finn earthside. It never occurred to me to let time pass and trust my body will get there in perfect time. There was this unspoken feeling that every minute had to be productive. I "consented" but did not know the risks. At this point, I did not feel "no" was even an option.

A few hours later, a nurse came on shift, and I give her so much credit for changing the trajectory of this birth story. She walked with an aura of maternal wisdom and confidence. She quickly became attuned to where I was in labor and did not fret about keeping continuous fetal monitoring. She encouraged me to walk, change positions, and intermittently checked Finn's heartbeat. When I think of her, I think of how she held space for me to do the work of laboring by pushing back the unnecessary systemic hospital policies. I made the most progress with her in my support network.

When I started to feel the need to push, I was told to lay on my back. From my education as a physical therapist, I knew lying on my back blocked the movement of the sacrum and coccyx, which limits the amount of opening through the pelvic outlet. Gravity was also doing me no favors in this position. More importantly, at that moment, I wanted to stay on my knees, resting my upper body on the back of the inclined hospital bed, but I was not given a choice or an opportunity to trust my body. I was told I had to move onto my back and was told when and how to push. With so much sensory input coming from my surroundings, I struggled to stay connected with what was happening inside me.

Finn was born at 4:52 pm. "Great! I'll be home for dinner," exclaimed my doctor. I was happy for her. I imagine the on-call life is incredibly difficult. At the same time, I could not shake this feeling that this whole birth experience was contrived to make everything easier for the hospital, and the needs of my family and I were an afterthought.

Finn was flopped on my belly for a minute and then whisked away for cleaning and measuring. I remember the look on Jason's face, not knowing whether he should stay with me or go to Finn. I think a nurse must have told Jason to come over so he could take pictures of Finn. I was getting stitched while the measuring and cleaning were taking place. Finn was out of my line of sight, so instead, I watched Jason carefully for any sign that something could be wrong. At the moment, I should have been happiest, I felt helpless. I could hear a healthcare worker joking about a husband stitch in the background, but all of my attention was on Jason and our baby that I could not see.

Eventually, the hustle and bustle ended, and it was finally Jason, Finn, and I. At least for a few minutes until the next temperature check or blood pressure check—there was always something that needed to be checked just as I was starting to drift asleep. We came home from the hospital exhausted.

Rowan's Rainbow Home Birth Story

When it came to choosing a midwife in Madison, I was torn between hospital-based and home. I did not know what home could be like or know any parents who had their baby at home. I am not exactly sure what led me to set up an interview with a local home birth midwife. I think I liked the idea of not driving anywhere and not being away from Finn for several nights. Little did I know that the benefits of home would FAR exceed my expectations.

I set up an interview with Ingrid Andersson RN, CNM, MS. What a difference in atmosphere! The space was calm, warm, and inviting. I instantly felt at ease and unexpectedly shared Finn's birth story for the first time. Ingrid did not pass any judgment, listened, and validated my experience. Was this what it is like to have your voice heard? She explained the philosophy of midwifery care, what to expect from prenatal and postnatal appointments. We talked about what birth at home can look like. We talked about the rate of transfers to the hospital and what that looks like if needed. She told me how many births she does per month and when she books up. She did not expect a decision at that interview, but I knew my mind was already made up—we would be planning a home birth.

This second pregnancy, unfortunately, ended in a miscarriage; however, I am incredibly grateful I was with the care of a home birth midwife when I experienced this. In true midwifery fashion, all of my options were laid out clearly, and I was given the space to make the right decision for my family. Beyond addressing the physical needs, she also checked in on me and said the most profound words. Ingrid said, "Be kind to yourself - there is nothing you did or can do to change the course of events... A miscarriage is like a birth. Your body knows how to do it and is no doubt wise in taking this path, even if there are no certain answers as to why." During a time I was experiencing so much grief, I also experienced so much comfort and compassion from my midwife.

When we felt emotionally ready to attempt a third pregnancy, I spent extra time and energy monitoring my cycles. My first birth taught me how many decisions get made on a somewhat arbitrary date—the due date. I think it should be called a guess date since less than 5% of people give birth to their babies on their due date. Due dates are often calculated based on your last missed period. This calculation assumes a 28-day cycle and ovulation occurring on day 14. I did not want to leave so many decisions to chance, so for subsequent pregnancies, I took my basal body temperature daily to know when ovulation actually occurred. It turns out I tend to ovulate on day 17 or 18 in a 31-day cycle.

With a more accurate guess date in hand, it was time to start my prenatal appointments with Ingrid and Miranda, a student midwife at the time of this story. (Miranda is now a licensed incredible midwife with her own practice.) These appointments were my favorite. Jason and Finn were always welcome. There was a playspace that Finn adored and would get lost in imaginary play as I talked for an hour—a full hour!—about the physical, mental, and nutritional aspects of my care. It was the most comprehensive holistic care I have ever received in my thirty years of life.

Knowing I was GBS positive in my first pregnancy, we spent time working towards a preventative approach. We talked about supplements, probiotic foods, and prebiotic foods (a completely new concept for me). I had an a-ha moment of realizing Finn probably was not "just a colicky baby" but had actually been reacting to the broad-spectrum antibiotic I received in labor. It now made sense why the probiotic made such a difference for Finn as a newborn. Having the time to discuss nutrition in-depth, I had hope for the first time that our baby on the way might be able to lay down without inconsolable crying. I had a glimmer of hope that maybe, just maybe, I might even enjoy the newborn days.

Throughout my pregnancy, we worked through an informed choices worksheet. We talked about the benefits, risks, and information that can be gained from every aspect of prenatal and newborn care, from ultrasounds to vitamin K administration and everything in between. I had time to ask questions, go home and process the information, then come back and ask more questions. While Jason and I overwhelmingly selected what is considered standard of care, I finally had the opportunity to consent to each aspect of my prenatal and postnatal care in a fully informed manner. I knew "no" was always an option. For the first time in my life, I felt respected and given the autonomy to make my own healthcare decisions.

At 36 weeks, Ingrid and Miranda came to our house. I showed them around the house. We double-checked I had everything I needed within the birth kit. Of course, we also checked on the baby, and I got to hear that sweet little fluttering heartbeat in my own home. Ingrid also spent time talking with Jason on what to do if the baby arrives before they would arrive and gave him a handout with the information as well. I highly doubted that would happen. I did appreciate the thoroughness, and Jason hung the sheet in a prominent spot on our refrigerator right next to the sheet that had our birth teams' phone numbers.

As my guess date neared, I began feeling nervous my body would not know how to go into labor. Since I was induced with Finn, I did not know what the early signs of labor felt like. During those last prenatal appointments, we spent quite a bit of time addressing my mental health. Ingrid and Miranda taught me a bit about belly mapping, giving me more ways to connect with my tiny growing babe. Ingrid also gave me a beautiful article to read about embracing that in between space, the space between your old and new self, the space between what is familiar and what is about to be. The article was called "The Last Days of Pregnancy: A Place of In-Between" by Jana Studelska CPM/LM. It is a beautiful read—I highly recommend it!

On Wednesday, three days before my guess date, I went to the zoo with a friend and her boys. Little did I know that would be my last adventure as a family of three. Around dinner time, I started feeling some waves. Every wave gave me a little jolt of excitement and a little seed of hope that perhaps my body did know how to give birth. Then with every stretch of time with no power-wraps[7], I sighed, feeling a bit deflated. The waves did not last long, and there was no discernible pattern. I wondered if this was prodromal labor. Around 11 pm, I called Ingrid, feeling confused because this was the most power-wraps I felt in one night, but they were not getting stronger or closer together. I could still breathe and talk through each wave. She encouraged me to try to rest and that if tonight is the night, the power-wraps will keep coming.

Every step of the way, she believed in my body's ability to birth even when I doubted myself.

I laid down for about an hour but could not sleep. I texted my mom and my friend and birth photographer, Raisa, to keep them updated as they had the furthest to travel. They both encouraged me to try to rest a bit too. Around midnight I moved to the rocking chair to try to sleep there. I was uncomfortable, so I decided to take a hot shower. I should have realized all of this moving around was early labor, but it was not at all how I imagined or how the books led me to believe.

After my shower, I tried to rest in the rocking chair again, but that was not comfortable either. The power-wraps were getting definitively stronger, and I found myself not wanting to leave the toilet. Jason came in, rubbed my back, and I started crying that I did not feel like a beautiful birth goddess. I had read a lot of birth stories about shifting your mindset to have this spiritual experience, but here I was on the toilet with diarrhea, in my dad's baseball shirt because no other shirt fit me, and cursing the author's name of all of those spiritual birth books.

Around 12:50 am, I told Jason I think he should call the birth team. He called Ingrid, my mom, Raisa, and my neighbor, Alice. Alice and her daughter, Lucy, so sweetly offered to be on call to play with Finn, get snacks for him, and help Finn feel part of the process with important jobs like holding the flashlight until my mom could arrive. As it turned out, this was never needed as Finn slept through the entire labor and birth.

With my birth team on their way, Jason drifted between picking up toys so I would have space to labor in our living room and rubbing my back as I sat on the toilet. The waves were now strong enough I had to vocalize through each power-wrap.

A little after 1 am, I experienced the fetal ejection reflex, which was this wild involuntary squeeze. The first squeeze caused me to stand up as I could feel Rowan move down into the birth canal. I tried to slow the moment down. Rowan, however, was not waiting for anyone. With the next wave, Rowan was born into the arms of his dad. I sat back down on the toilet and held Rowan skin to skin, stunned and amazed—we did it.

I remember the gratitude I felt for the time Ingrid and Miranda spent teaching us what to do if our baby arrives before their arrival. The education we received made this precipitous labor and delivery feel beautiful and empowering. It is interesting to think how regardless of what we planned, Rowan would have been born at home. This birth would have certainly involved an ambulance ride had we planned a hospital birth. Instead, I was safe in my home with my support team already en route and seconds away. Jason and I felt so much pride in what we accomplished. Knowledge is powerful.

The next bit was a whirl of somewhat comedic events. Alice was the first to arrive, not surprisingly, as she lived across the street. It was surprising for us all that instead of being in labor, I was introducing her to my son as I sat naked on the toilet with his cord still pulsating. Ingrid showed up a minute later with the warmest expression, almost as if to say, "she did it, just as I knew she would, just as so many birthing people before her." No words were exchanged that I can remember, but that is what I imagined in my head. Jason called my mom and Raisa to let them know they could stay home as Rowan had already arrived. While this was not how I imagined my birth to go, I felt supported, and my autonomy was honored every step of the way.

The perks of having my baby at home really shined during the postpartum time. The night of Rowan's birth, I spent his first hour earthside just taking in every adorable wrinkle as he nursed, and we cuddled skin to skin in my own bed. I truly got my golden hour. It was the best hour of my life. It was not until Rowan took a break from breastfeeding that we did all the measuring, neuro screen, and looking over the magnificent placenta together. I got to see and be a part of every moment. There were no competing demands. It felt as if our whole birth team was working in perfect harmony to hold space as we gently landed from the space of bringing life into the world, a space that fondly gets referred to as laborland. This was person-centered care.

Before leaving for the night, Ingrid and Miranda expertly rearranged furniture and created a better functioning "nest" for our newborn days. Now I had a table next to my bed with water, snacks, diapers, wipes, goldenseal for the umbilical cord, and a night light to make nighttime feeding and diaper changes quiet and serene. They stocked my freezer with homemade padsicles and filled a peri bottle by the toilet with anti-inflammatory and anti-infective herbal tea. The heat was turned up in the house, the heavy comforter on our bed removed, and the bed set up to facilitate safe bedsharing as they knew that was our preferred sleeping arrangement.

I awoke the next morning feeling revitalized. There was no evidence a birth even occurred other than this tiny little human in our bed.

For the first six weeks, we did not drive anywhere. Ingrid and Miranda came to our home to check on Rowan and me. Each visit often lasted longer than an hour in order to cover all the immense physical and emotional changes. On day three, they opened the door to discussions that are often only briefly glossed over at the six-week appointment in the hospital setting by acknowledging this tends to be the start of an emotionally charged time due to shifting hormones. Having developed a secure relationship over the course of pregnancy, I felt I could be vulnerable and have honest conversations about anxiety earlier in my postpartum journey.

Moving Forward and Improving Birth Culture

My home birth experience was not only healing and validating; it also showed me what healthcare should look like as a consumer and what to strive for as a healthcare provider. Many healthcare providers hide behind the philosophy of evidence-based care that all decisions should be made based on the latest research. We need to shift this mindset. Evidence-based care is only the first layer. Healthcare providers need to go beyond this by presenting the evidence and then expecting the consumer will make their own healthcare decisions. These decisions will likely be influenced by the consumer's values, and priorities in addition to the evidence presented. This is informed decision-making. Providing evidence-based care alone is not enough.

From my experience, it feels hospitals have become so accustomed to medically managed birth, it failed me in being unable to provide care for normal physiologic birth. I felt my providers in the hospital did not know how not to intervene. They did not know how to hold space for a birthing person and be a lifeguard only if complications arose. They did not know how to or did not feel comfortable in catching a baby in any position other than the dorsal lithotomy position[8].

I chose home because I did not want my birth treated as a medical emergency. By choosing home, I was ensuring autonomy in making my own healthcare decisions. I was ensuring I did not have to fight systemic hospital policies that place priority on efficiency, capital gain, and avoiding litigation over the needs of my family and me.

I chose home because it is safe. Many studies consistently demonstrate that birth at home with a licensed midwife has no increase in adverse outcomes and results in fewer unnecessary interventions.

I chose home so I could labor on my own schedule. I was able to keep my attention inward and focus on responding to my own bodily cues without any competing advice.

Home is cozy and birth being the hormonally driven process it is, it makes sense birth proceeds optimally in this familiar environment. Home is where life happens. Why not birth?

We could transform our birth culture and improve birth outcomes by honoring the wisdom of the birthing person and by building a birth team that excels in perinatal health. Midwives should be the standard of care for pregnant people. Midwives are the experts in pregnancy, birth, and breastfeeding. They are experts in the normal physiologic birth process and the prevention of complications. According to the World Health Organization, the midwifery approach reduces maternal and neonatal adverse outcomes, reduces unnecessary interventions, improves satisfaction for birthing families, and is cost-effective. Countries with the best maternal and neonatal outcomes are led by midwives. Obstetricians co-manage high-risk pregnancies, which is better suited to their medical training. This collaborative approach optimizes birth outcomes by leaning into the strengths of each profession yet ultimately leading with the midwifery model of care.

Physical therapy is another resource that enhances the care received during pregnancy and the postpartum journey. Pregnancy and birth are a time in life where the body goes through tremendous musculoskeletal changes, and physical therapists are the experts in the musculoskeletal system and movement. Movement during pregnancy and labor has been shown to improve birth outcomes significantly. Specifically, movement during labor allows for more effective uterine muscle contractions, shortens labor, improves comfort, and gives the birthing person a better sense of control.

A physical therapist (PT) can support a birthing person by providing education on biomechanics and movement strategies during every phase of the pregnancy journey. Prenatally, movement education can assist a birthing person for this time when your center of gravity is shifting, and the length tension relationship of muscles are elongating. PTs can help alleviate low back pain and pelvic discomfort that may occur during this time. PTs can also provide education prenatally on labor movement strategies to optimize pelvic joint mobility and pelvic floor muscle coordination and relaxation. Then in the postpartum time movement education can facilitate healing.

We need to start actively encouraging movement during labor and normalizing the vast array of birthing positions. Hands and knees, side-lying, squatting, sitting on a birthing seat, kneeling are all great options to allow the joints of the pelvis and sacrum to move and shift optimally as well as maximize the openings of the pelvic inlet and outlet. Use gravity to your advantage! If you are compelled to move into asymmetric positions such as bringing one leg forward or back or to the side, follow those instincts. Since the baby often rotates during its descent, it makes sense asymmetric positioning could facilitate this rotation. Most importantly, trust your body. Only you and your baby know the steps to this dance of bringing your baby earthside. Follow your intuition.

During the postpartum time, many will remark on peeing their pants when sneezing, laughing, or during exercise. While common, it is treatable. You do not need to live with peeing your pants, even if it is just a little bit. Pelvic floor physical therapists can treat pelvic pain, changes in bowel and bladder such as incontinence and gas leakage, pelvic organ prolapse, pain with sex, scar sensitivity, and returning to exercise. In France, it is standard of care to receive perineal rehabilitation postpartum. We could be doing so much more to take care of new parents. I often tell my friends to skip asking for another baby outfit at your baby shower and instead ask for a gift certificate to see your local pelvic floor physical therapist during your fourth trimester.

I hope this story inspires you to see what is possible. Not in the sense that every home birth will resemble this birth story. Just by reading this book, you will see that is far from true. Your story, perhaps already unfolded or yet to unfold, will be yours and only yours. I hope this story will serve as an example of the care and support that is possible and that you deserve. You are the expert of your own body. You deserve to be supported during this sacred time. You have the right to ask questions, and you have the right to say no. Find a healthcare team that honors your inner wisdom. Your birth experience matters. You matter. You got this.

-----

1. **guess date:** synonym for due date
2. **Pitocin:** a hormone used to induce contractions
3. **Cervidil:** a hormone used to dilate the cervix
4. **continuous fetal monitoring:** a sensor that records baby's heartbeat at all times
5. **tachycardic:** rapid heart rate
6. **waves:** description referring to tightening and relaxing of the uterine muscle during labor
7. **power-wrap:** description referring to tightening and relaxing of the uterine muscle during labor
8. **dorsal lithotomy position:** laying semi-reclined on your back with your hips and knees flexed and feet in footrests

DR. AMANDA CLEARY PICKART PT, DPT

Amanda was born and raised in Wisconsin. She received her B.A. in psychology and Portuguese at the University of Wisconsin-Madison. She lived a year in Portugal. She then went on to complete her Doctorate of Physical Therapy at the University of Wisconsin-Madison. She has worked in various settings, including a skilled nursing facility, hospital, and an outpatient clinic, where she incorporated hippotherapy into her treatment plans. It was in this last setting she became fascinated with the role of the pelvis and pelvic floor muscles in rehabilitation. She aspires to move into the obstetric and pelvic floor physical therapy specialties.

Amanda enjoys helping others heal through movement. She hopes the benefits of movement during labor and the spectrum of birthing positions possible become more widely recognized and normalized. She believes every pregnancy journey deserves continuous informed support.

Amanda loves to hike and is an avid equestrian. She especially loves to adventure in the outdoors with her husband, Jason, and their three sweet children, Finn, Rowan, and Sage.

Website: http://birthingpositions.com

E-mail: amandapickartphysio@gmail.com

Ingrid Andersson LM, CNM, MSN
Community Midwives, LLC
http://www.communitymidwives.info/

Miranda Welch LM, CPM
Grassrootsmidwifery, LLC
https://grassrootsmidwifery.com/

Madison Area Midwives: http://www.madisonmidwives.com/

Photography by Raisa:
https://photographybyraisa.com/

8

RISING EMPOWERMENT

TWO HOSPITAL BIRTHS AND ONE HOMEBIRTH.

YAEL JULANOV C.HP, CHT

My Roots, miscarriage, and battle with infertility

As a child, I was all too curious about how people ran their lives and what their experiences did for them. I was that five-year-old kid in the park that asked a stranger, "Where do babies come from." Persistence helped me get an answer too! My grandparents were from Russia, and I admired stories of their natural lifestyle. Coming to America threw everyone off course. However, glimpses into that life kept thrusting me back into trusting that there must be a more natural and safe way for pregnancy, birth, and everything else in life. They imparted a message of how birth isn't something to be feared. Rather, it's a process to go through with loving, supportive people around you. In my modern lens of the world, I was under the impression that you get that support in the hospital scene since so many people I spoke with liked their hospital experiences. I learned that wasn't always the case soon enough.

So, how did I get here? I'll tell ya. It all started when I was 22 years old and newly married. Man was I up for shell shock. I was blissfully happy for a moment until it was interrupted by the storm of a miscarriage. I wasn't ready for that, and frankly, I don't think anyone ever is at any given point in their life. It was a short-lived pregnancy and a very difficult three-day process to fully pass on the baby at home. That miscarriage left me bruised and scarred emotionally and physically. We decided to try again right away, but something was different. It just wasn't happening. I went to see my OBGYN, and that was the moment when I learned just how damaging my miscarriage was. It completely turned my hormones around, and I developed a condition—the all too famous Polycystic Ovarian Syndrome, known as PCOS in short. I had too many cysts, and my follicles were too immature. Suddenly, all the post-miscarriage pains I had been dealing with made sense to me. The worst part was I couldn't conceive on my own. The news came at me like a ton of bricks. My emotional rollercoaster is hard to describe. How did I go from feeling a sense of validation of all the pain I'd been through to walking out with despair? It was too much to take, and I needed time to pace myself. I took a month off until I would try my doctor's suggestions. I took that time just to be and reflect within me. I took some time to prepare my body and spirit for this new journey I was about to embark on. No one else in my family had experienced infertility, so I was alone here. I needed to just be still for a little bit.

My doctor gave me two choices to deal with PCOS. Go on birth control or take Clomid if you want to conceive. I opted for Clomid. Before I could do that, I had to take Metformin which was an awful experience for me. I developed a rare side effect called lactic acidosis. I was so weak I felt like I was struggling to breathe. My doctor told me to get off it immediately, and if anything got worse to head to the emergency room. This was an experience that made me more wary and hesitant to just blindly take medications ever again. From now on, I would be checking side effects out first and then checking within myself if my body was sending off signals that maybe this isn't for me. Each experience brought me to a place of new understanding and awareness of what's going on around me and within. I learned I could make my own rules. By becoming a conscious creator of my life experience, here, empowerment was born. I decided to try another route to help my overall health and balance out my hormones. I decided to start eating more wholesome foods. Foods that support hormones such as yams, meats, and loads of veggies. I looked to more warming foods such as pomegranates and cinnamon. Goodbye sugar and processed foods. Junk was off the table! I went to an acupuncturist who told me how hot my liver was. I had so much fire in me; don't I know it!

A few sessions in, and I felt like a calmer person. My cycle that month was easy, I felt a shift in me, and so I started my Clomid round. It wasn't easy feeling like all my eggs were making their way out at the same time. I was bloated, emotionally fragile, and tired. Somehow, I felt strong enough to get through this part. I prayed a lot and gave it over to God. This was our journey together—all three of us.

Complicated Twin pregnancy and birth

Luckily, I conceived, and it was twins. I was elated and terrified at the same time. It was a difficult, high-risk pregnancy. The all-day-and-night sickness was relentless. I was working at my day job in an office at the time, and I took bathroom breaks often to quell my nausea head over the toilet and to take a nap on the bathroom floor. I know, yuck! No one tells you how much more tired you are during a twin pregnancy! I kept spinning in and out of constant premature labor. Taking a short walk was enough to get it started. I was so fragile. By 18 weeks pregnant, I had to go on bedrest at home. I was really appalled by how my OBGYN at the time was handling our care. He hadn't remembered who I was even in my second or third trimester.

Red flags were going off everywhere as all he would ever talk about was a C-section from week seven and on. It was obvious he wasn't interested in giving me a chance to have a natural birth. To deal with the constant premature labor, I was drinking an ounce of wine a day to stop the labor since 29 weeks. That was immensely helpful until the one night I had no more wine! My awful OB did not care that my bloody mucus plug came out. He said it was fine and unless I was in real labor not to bother. I was very confused here. Why was he waiting for it to be too late to stop the labor? I went to research while feeling huge and fatigued, and everything I read showed me again just how incompetent this doctor was.

I decided to change OBGYN practices. I had an appointment that Monday at last. Just one day away, on Sunday at 31 weeks and 5 days pregnant, my labor wouldn't stop despite trying several things to make the labor stop. We called for an ambulance to take me to the hospital. They couldn't stop the labor either, and because I officially had no OBGYN, I was at the mercy of the hospital staff. I had no idea what was waiting for me—all the bullying. The male doctors were getting angry with me and very roughly checking my cervix to teach me compliance. They all thought they would tire me into their demands. My twin girls and I were doing wonderfully. Not once did any of us show we were in any medical, physical distress, yet they demanded with scare tactics and pressure that I must commit to a c-section. A confirmed rumor was that the head of L&D wanted me for production that day, and so every OBGYN was pushed through that door to scare me and force me one way or another. Every time they came into my room, my sister did an excellent job asking them to repeat themselves repeatedly, eventually out annoying them. The one time they didn't harass me was when I was having the epidural procedure done. They probably didn't want what would be an obvious lawsuit. I loathed the way the hospital staff was treating me. The obnoxious comments, physically aggressively handling of my body, all the bullying and pressurizing me to admit to a c section when something in my heart was just telling me, "No, don't do this because you won't survive that." I turned to my faith and prayed to God for support and strength for myself and my twin babies.

After ten grueling hours of the nonstop bullying, at last, a doctor came in that told me I could have my twins naturally. It turned out that baby A was head down, but baby B was breech, yet that was not a reason to jump into a c-section. Preemies can get stuck in the birth canal if not fully dilated. All I needed to make sure of was that I was fully dilated as the babies' heads weren't big and strong enough to push through and open up the last centimeter of the cervix. One thought kept coming to mind. I remembered my grandmother. She had five different breech babies, all of whom she birthed naturally. If my grandma can give birth to five different breech babies at home safely, then I can do this. I tried to remember that although ALL the male staff, in particular, were obnoxious and felt that they were experts, there was one thing I had on them that they didn't possess. I was a woman. They had no idea what it is was like to embody and be a woman. They could not do what I could do, and so they had no idea what I was feeling or capable of.

Finally, at better peace, two hours later, we made significant progress. I was 9 cm dilated, and my savior OB gave me Pitocin to get me to 10 cm. I was fully ready to have my babies. The moment was very bitter-sweet. There was a glimpse of triumph in that I can birth these babies with a competent and compassionate OB who supports my body, and yet I was grieving the end of this pregnancy. This was going to be the end of our shared body time together. I felt like a failure. I let them down by having them so early, and I was so sorry. The NICU experience was something neither of us will ever forget, but that's for another chapter!

I was only allowed to bring in one person with me to the operating birthing room. One of the most embarrassing parts was when there were over 30 people in the room, more than half of them not included in any way for my birth, just there to see if the stubborn lady actually got her way and was she right about it. Would my decisions lead to success or an epic fail? I was in a fight over who was right, the doctors or I? The experts or the plain regular first-time mom? With my sister by my side, I pushed out baby A in just a few minutes. My savior OB put on the longest hand and arm glove they had and went to fish baby B out by both her feet. I never thought I would have a human hand swim that far up my body. I felt her hand right under my heart. She caught both feet, and I pushed continuously, and that was it. Baby B was born just 6 minutes younger than her older twin sister. I was in and out of there in 20 minutes. It can be done, and I did it. My intuition was strong, and what I knew about myself no one else could know. I held onto that. I wanted responsible healthcare with my best interests in mind, and I got it, but not without a fight. That thought always stung and stayed with me. It shouldn't have to be that way. It shouldn't be this hard. I wanted to feel like a valued patient, not another vacations worth for them. Despite my apparent success, the hospital still tried to make me feel worthless with comments and sent in a social worker to see if I was OK because I had worked that hard to refuse a c-section. Of course, I was OK. I was better than OK. I was fighting for better than most of the people that I encountered there, and maybe that was my "crime."

I had suffered a major loss of blood during the birth. I was left with half my blood volume. This is where I thanked myself for sticking up to what felt right for me. I could not imagine had I gotten the surgery if I would've walked out of there at all. While in recovery, no one brought me down to see my girls. Not even an update. Two days later, while bleeding heavily, epidural still wearing off, and feeling dizzy, I wobbled my way to the NICU myself. No one offered any care despite seeing me in this condition. Beyond that, I was so embarrassed that, as a new mom, I could not tell who my children were. After the birth, I got a two-second glimpse, and then they whisked them away. Seeing them so small and so brave this young can only be described with one word. A waterfall. It's serenity so peaceful and its force so powerful. They were already larger than life itself.

Prepared 2nd hospital birth with my son

I had triumphed an exceptionally large victory, and yet I felt a massive loss. A loss of human decency, faith in the medical establishment, respect for my body, and a loving experience. Why was I at war when I was doing the most loving thing any human can do? Giving life selflessly to another human being. I should've been honored, and yet I was battered instead. I fought hard and won ultimately, but it came at a very heavy toll emotionally. I bore wounds that were raw and fresh for a long time. These feelings of doubt and hospital trauma carried on within me onto my next pregnancy with my son. I had doubts about myself and felt I wasn't quite ready for a homebirth. I needed to see my body work at full speed by itself. That meant getting pregnant on my own with no mainstream medicine help or extensive supportive measures, staying pregnant until full term, and giving birth without an epidural. That was enough of a change for me to work through.

I tried to create a fusion of the two medical worlds. This time I wanted to be prepared. I wanted to release all the doubt and uncertainty that had crept in. Underneath all that anger was sadness. This was my way of trying to give myself and the hospital another chance. I wanted to forgive them and myself.

I hired a wonderful doula who was supportive and deeply knowledgeable. I also opted for a hospital birth with a midwife who was part of an OBGYN practice. I wanted to be as responsible as I could be and cover all my bases. The pregnancy was a unique one of its own. I struggled with the fear of having another preemie. I had gotten pregnant just a year and a half since I had the twins, and so I did not feel like I recovered just yet. Meanwhile, I had adopted a more

natural lifestyle to support this pregnancy. I cleaned up my immediate environment as much as I could. My journey with homeopathy
started here. I switched to organic foods and products. I used essential oils and other holistic methods for every ail. I took enzymes this
time instead of Tums. I saw every message the body was giving me as
a sign for further improvement. I wanted to appreciate my body and
for it to appreciate me back. My body is my best friend, and I decided
to start treating it as such. Who else was going to work this hard
for me?

The day of the birth arrived at 39 weeks and 1 day. I made it to full
term, and I felt a sense of confidence wash over me. It was interrupted by the midwife going on vacation during the last week of my
pregnancy (how rude). The OBGYN of that practice who I got to
meet once came for the delivery. I wasn't very comfortable because
we only met once, but I did know enough about him, and I felt
comfortable in my reasons for choosing him in the emergency
scenario. Although this is my 3rd child, it was my second time giving
birth. Those are usually said to be much faster, and it was a very
quick birth for us. He was born an hour after we arrived at the hospital. I went from 4 cm at check-in to delivering in an hour.

I was enjoying the hot shower to help me through the intense
contractions, and I was told to come out so they could put a very tight
belly band on me. They were trying to get an IV line in while I was in
transition. It was torture trying to stay still for that. I just barely
climbed onto the birthing bed. I had very intense back labor, and
laying on my back was another added torture I did not want. My
mind was still in that shower. That's where my body and mind
wanted to be. I felt connected to the running water. My doula, Chloe,
was very sweet and supportive. I could tell she was upset for me yet
confident. She was my rock there. The doctor came in and while for
the most part he was decent, there seems to be a common disconnect
between many professionals. When a woman tells you she does not
want to be touched, it's simple. Do not touch her. When a woman

says I don't want to be checked, it's simple. Do not check her against her will. I am fairly sure this isn't rocket science, but where is informed consent in all of this? I asked him not to touch me. I was in transition. I just knew it. I needed to focus, and he was intervening where I didn't need him to.

Just as I looked the other way to breathe through, he checked me, and, in my shock, I gasped in despair. The nurse and doula couldn't tell what that was from, and neither did he. Feelings and memories of feeling traumatized and violated from the last birth came flooding in. Why? That was all I could ask. Why? Why was this happening to me again? I chose this doctor. I had been so responsible. Why is it so hard to get the kind of care you need? Why can't they respect your needs and respect consent? These weren't the feelings and thoughts I wanted to hold while suddenly pushing out my son in lightning speed. Invoking feelings of anxiety were not on the birth plan until I was disrespected. In one swift motion, I went from empowered to disempowered. We are all different people with vastly different life experiences and personalities. Some of us go through a lot of trauma, and many medical doctors just don't take that into account. Consent is supposed to protect us. A one size fits all approach does not work. The mother's mental well-being is just as important as her physical well-being. We are all so different, and so consent to everything is so crucial. My wise midwife once said that it's an art to know when not to touch a patient during labor and birth. I wholeheartedly agree with her.

The hardest part about birthing in the hospital is that there are so many hospital policies that it leaves truly little room for professional and common-sense practice. Medical professionals can't be at their best at the expense of their patients because of all the policies in place.

I got tired of them whisking my son away for hours despite me asking them to leave him with me because we were exclusively breastfeeding. Weighing him alone took two hours, and they got that wrong too. I got a more accurate weight just by weighing him on my hands. I was tired of doing everything on their schedule and terms. I was tired of this, and my body had done enough proving to me.

I felt I needed to leave from there. I felt triggered all over the place. I forgave myself, but they made it awfully hard to forgive them. I did not need to extend the courtesy anymore. I can move on without them. With their permission, I decided to leave from there at the 24-hour mark. I was a pro mom at this point, having nursed two preemies to health. If anyone had this, it was me. I was going to use all my holistic tools to help myself heal. All the bruising, tears, and bleeding healed much faster with it. Arnica and other homeopathic remedies were here to my rescue so gently yet effectively. My son did wonderfully at home, no longer separated from me. We enjoyed an exceptionally long breastfeeding journey together. Feelings of bliss and safety were at home, and I wanted to have a homebirth the next time I had a child. I wanted to expound on these feelings from the very start to finish. What I didn't know was that those feelings never dissipate. It's been five years since my homebirth, and I still feel bliss every time I think about the homebirth. Every time I see my son, these feelings are mutually shared. We both well up in joy. Your start in life is going to be part of your journey for a very long time. I see that clearly, having tried three different ways to go about this.

Inspired and healing home birth with my son

Ten months after my son's hospital birth, I was pregnant again. I guess when it rains, it pours. Remember I used to be infertile? Well, this time, the birth control didn't work. I'm glad it didn't. This was one of the most profound and healing moments of my life. I take it with me always. Not only was my son born, but I was reborn as a new mother and a renewed being in many places where my heart and spirit were hurting.

Feeling more fed up and confident, I started researching for a home-birth midwife. I was determined to find someone that my gut instinct told me was good for me. At seven weeks pregnant, I had my first meeting with Kristin. With a questionnaire in hand, we got through everything and more. It was simple, and it was focused on me. She exuded so much warmth and intelligence that I was blown away. In some ways, she reminded me of my savior OBGYN, who relocated to Florida shortly after the twin's birth. There was the feeling of sister-hood and care. She was looking out for me in a personal and profes-sional capacity. Birth is personal, and so it stands to hold that energy. I was more than happy with our meeting, and my intuition was singing happy tunes. I decided to hire Kristin and my former doula Chloe. I had a powerhouse of a team by my side. Every visit was in my home. The personal attention meant everything. I was being listened to and got really good care that was individual to my needs without compromising anything. I loved the higher standards of care and the respect of the intimate role a pregnancy and birth are.

This pregnancy was by far the healthiest one I had. Not a glimmer of morning sickness and premature labor. I was as healthy as a horse. I managed to stay pregnant, co-sleep, and nurse my son throughout the entire pregnancy. This year, in particular, was full of changes. We moved and got more intensely involved in our twins' recovery and healing from being preemies and surviving the NICU. I had never been this productive while pregnant. I attribute that to my holistic lifestyle and the care I was receiving from my midwife and doula. I realized that every visit was simply a pleasure. It was not anxiety driven with scare tactics. Every moment of the way, consent was asked for everything. Kristin listened to me and eased my heart when-ever I seemed to need a listening ear, be it for whatever ailed me at the moment. Knowing that I was in competent hands and a warm heart meant everything to me. At 40 weeks and 4 days, I said to my baby, it's time to come out. I believe in our mind-body connections to be very real and strong. With each baby, I had conversations saying just how much of a team we are. We are in this together, and the only way through is together. I had asked my first son to please at least make it to 39 weeks and 1 day, and he did. That morning labor started. The same thing happened here. We made a deal by 40 weeks and 4 days, we were ready. Kristin and Chloe came packed and ready. I spent some time laboring around my bedroom while my husband spent all the time with our little kids. He finally took them to the park so I could concentrate on my birth and not get frazzled by every tantrum my kids made, which were many!

I was a pro at this by now. I knew exactly what I wanted. After about two hours, I decided I was going to get into a hot shower. I remembered just how much I loved the feeling of the hot water running down my back. I labored there in the dim light without any interruptions for 2 hours. Chloe and Kristin were at my constant beck and call. Giving me water, fanning me with towels for extra air, handing me whatever I needed, listening, and providing. My amazing therapist at the time told me just how triggering birth can be for people who have trauma. With his wisdom in mind, every contraction felt like a wave of opportunity as I thought about all the trauma that happened to me. The energy of the experience was high, and I wanted to use this moment to release all that pain. I thought and cried and laughed a little. It was a huge mixed bag of emotions, and everything was game at this point. My childhood flashed before my eyes. All my experiences in the hospital were moving through me. I let them go as I exhaled every breath and cried on the shower tiles. This was the most exhilarating experience I ever had. I was giving birth to a new human being. I was becoming a new mother again, and I was also reborn through the release of my old traumas.

I knew I was in transition when I said, "Ok, how do I get the hell outta here?" I just want to be done. Can I somehow separate myself from the labor and birth? Realizing that there is nowhere to go but through this, I laid down a towel. My mind and body went primal. I was preparing for my baby's landing. I got down on all four hands and knees and went into what felt like a meditative space of mind. I prayed and cried and felt a higher power take charge. I started to push instinctually as Kristin was by my side, watching me and guiding me as I needed. The room was filled with whispers, soft lights, pleasant aromas, and a sense of safety and calm. I was home, and so was my baby after three solid pushes. He gently cried, and I lifted him to my chest, holding this wonderment. I loved how I was the very first person to touch and hold him. He was my baby, after all, and after nine months of pregnancy and a birth, I think I deserved that honor more than anyone else. I was primal and protective. The first person I wanted my baby to feel was me. I wanted him to feel the warmth of my heart and the tenderness of my arms as he took his first breaths. We were one unit during the pregnancy, and we were one unity during the birth. Both of us feeling in harmony with our existence and environment. I stayed in that shower with the water off for a whole hour. There was no rush to finish anything. These were the priceless first moments that are the most powerful force of bonding between mother and child. He will always go here, and so will I. This is home, and that's where we were in our hearts and bodies.

I got to cut his cord, and he nursed again out of the shower. Kristin and Chloe stayed with me for another two hours, making sure that the baby and I were well and cared for. We had all the necessary medical checks and care we needed without the stress and extra interventions. Not once did I feel violated by my midwife or doula. They never once did something that I didn't need them to. My recovery was wonderful. I spent zero time trying to recover from this birth mentally and emotionally. It had healed me instead.

I did not suffer, and that meant everything to my family and me. It changed me in more ways than I can count. The entire experience from start to finish was one where my intuition and body led the way. I loved how deeply this was respected. I did not have to fight to keep reclaiming my inner voice and humanity. I was a newly empowered woman and mother without the scars and wounds. My homebirth experience is my happy place that I go to when I need to feel safe.

As my wise midwife said," There is pain during a homebirth, but there is no suffering."

YAEL JULANOV C.HP, CHT

Yael Julanov is a Homeopath, Homeoprophylaxis supervisor, Certified in Homeopathic Detox and Drainage integrating CEASE therapy, Detox consultant, and Gemmotherapy practitioner. Originally from Russia, she immigrated to NY as a 3-year-old child with her parents and siblings. Allergies were a foreign concept and seeing a friend at the park that was allergic to strawberries was a hard pill to swallow. Seeing the stark differences in the health of Americans versus Russians was one reason why she took the initiative to live a more natural lifestyle like that of her grandparents. Yael lives in New York with her husband and their four children. Her children's health challenges were the driving force for Yael to learn all things holistic. She spent years learning and helping her children recover from a variety of health issues. She believes in a wholesome and holistic approach to meet the wellness needs of clients of all ages to bring them back to balance. Yael's passion is to empower families with health, information, and confidence to care for their loved ones and beyond.

Website: Thepurplewell.com
Email: YaelHB21@gmail.com

Representing FHCi and can be found there-Freeandhealthychil-
dren.org under supervisors
Chloe website - www.wildrootmidwifery.com

9

CHOOSING MY WAY
ONE HOSPITAL BIRTH, ONE HOME BIRTH, AND NATURAL
MOVEMENT

ANNE HANCOCK

Background

I MET MY HUSBAND, Rock, when I was single and living the active, young professional life in Washington DC. I kept busy with happy hours, recreational sports, and the like. After a short courtship, we decided to take the plunge into cohabitating. As that adventure took off, we explored our joint passion for health and wellness. Rock had already been exploring how to improve wellness through diet for himself while trying to lose weight, and I began to settle into the notion that less is more on many fronts, including wellness. As our relationship grew stronger, I began to slowly entertain the notion of starting a family, even if it was still a way off. And if I wanted to start a family, I needed to start thinking about how I wanted to do that.

For some, the planning stages of starting a family may simply involve removing/stopping birth control. I had a few other things to consider. I had struggled with disordered eating, anxiety, and depression. And as a result, I had been on some combination of psychiatric medications since I was 16 years old. I was lucky that I got the support and attention I needed to get me through some tough times. I will admit that it never felt like depression wholly captured what I experienced, but that was a diagnosis that was something most people could understand. I was usually taking two to three different medications at a time, as well as seeing a therapist. I never thought there was any other way to manage my mental health and stay well. For some, this may be the best and safest way to manage it. Therapy is always a great help, no matter what else you combine with it. Yet, while I knew the medications had probably kept me alive up to that point, I did not love the idea of staying on them while pregnant, even if there is research to suggest some of them are safe. I wanted to at least try to see how I could manage without them. We had also been reading more and more research on the gut-brain connection. With immense support and knowledge from Rock as well as my therapists, we started the journey of healing my gut through some major diet changes to see if I could be stable off medication. I understood it might not work but felt it was worth a shot if it meant I could be stable enough to have kids while not on the medication. I will tell you—as someone with a history of disordered eating—I was terrified of implementing any sort of dietary restrictions. It simply made my anxiety go through the roof. But with lots of time to think it through, weighing the benefits, and asking myself - *What is the worst that could happen?* I realized the answer was not that scary, so I decided to go for it.

You may be wondering what this has to do with my birth story. Here is the main message that I hope you take away from my story: Never assume any decision or choice is the *only* choice. Seek out as much information as possible and make the decision that feels the most right for you and your family.

In my case, this started with making a different decision to manage my mental health than the one I had made for many years. That alternate choice took many years and a move to Madison, WI, but I was able to conceive my first son after being medication-free for over a year.

My Hospital Birth

When we started planning for my first son's birth, I did not question whether there was another option other than the hospital. That was all I knew.

I knew I wanted to try for a natural birth, and so in that vein, Rock and I signed up for a Bradley Method class as well as worked with a team of hospital-based midwives instead of an OB for our prenatal care. For those not familiar with the Bradley Method birth education classes, it was ten weeks, meeting once a week for two hours, for both partners. I loved it. And in the end, we ended up hiring our instructor as our doula since we liked her so much. She also offered placenta encapsulation. Since I had read that placenta consumption could help prevent postpartum depression, something I was very fearful of experiencing considering my mental health history, I wanted to do everything I could to support my body and mind. It is hard to know whether it helped me in the end, but I will tell you now that I did not experience postpartum depression.

My pregnancy was as smooth as it could be. I was very lucky in that until my belly started getting noticeable, even I could easily forget I was pregnant. All our visits with the hospital-based midwife team went swimmingly. I always came with lots of questions, and they usually had satisfactory and comforting answers. Each visit with the midwife was about 30 minutes, and while we did see a few of them on more than one occasion, we saw a different team member throughout the course of our prenatal care.

With plenty of time to spare, we had our birth plan laid out with what we did and didn't want in the hospital and made sure our midwife team had reviewed it. On my due date, I started having contractions around 3am and got quite excited. After an hour or more, the excitement faded as the contractions faded. I was mentally ready to have my baby, but apparently, my body and my baby were not ready. Our doula gave us some advice for some things to try—like walking with one foot on the curb and the other foot on the street—to help keep things moving, but alas, it was just false labor. Days passed, and I grew anxious.

At 41 weeks and a few days, we went in for a standard NST. The results weren't alarming, but they were borderline. The midwife we were seeing that day said they wanted us to check into the hospital for induction. My heart sank. That was the last thing I wanted. Yet, I had woken up that morning feeling depressed that I still hadn't had my baby. While I really didn't want to be induced, I felt that was what I had to do. I felt defeated and sad like somehow, I had failed already.

The midwife wanted us to check in to the hospital immediately. We pushed back. Begrudgingly, she accepted our promise to head back to the hospital after heading home first to gather our thoughts and things. At least in this instance, we didn't assume what the midwife wanted was the only option.

I cried on the drive home. I was worried about how everything would unfold. But I tried to focus on the positive: I would be meeting my baby very soon. Once we were back at the hospital and all checked in, the monitors indicated the baby was fine. Maybe the NST results were just a fluke. But at that point, we were at the hospital and emotionally ready to get the process started. There was no turning back.

After being examined, I was told that I needed a cervical ripening agent before anything else. We discussed a couple of options and decided to go with Cervidil, which is inserted like a tampon and could be taken out at any time. The Cervidil was inserted that evening and left in for 12 hours. I was told to get some rest. I'm sure I slept some, but the anticipation of labor made sleep difficult. Around the 10 hour mark, I started to have more regular contractions that seemed to be getting stronger. When it was time to remove the Cervidil, the contractions were progressing well enough that the midwife on shift agreed to let me labor with no further drugs so long as everything continued to progress. I was relieved. I felt hopeful that maybe I could labor on my own, and all my body needed was a little nudge. And sure enough, that's all I needed.

My sister arrived as planned, and the doula arrived a little later in the morning. Because I was induced, I need a pic line, per hospital protocol. This, both literally and figuratively, got under my skin. I really didn't want one because I thought for sure I would decline anything for which they would have needed an IV. But hospital protocols are hospital protocols. I had to move on and just focus on keeping labor going.

Labor continued to progress, and it was clear that I was going to be "enjoying" back labor, likely due to the baby's position. I labored in a variety of positions—thanks to wireless monitors—and never stayed in any one place for very long. I spent some time on the toilet, on hands and knees, and standing and leaning on Rock. I tried to labor some in a tub but could not get comfortable. My body started bearing down, but when I was checked, I was only 5cm dilated. So, I was told to try to breathe through it. This was probably the *most* impossible part of labor. But somehow, I did it.

After about ten hours of labor, I ended up in the bed, slightly on my side with my legs held up to try to shift the baby's position. I was far enough along at that point that I ended up staying there for delivery after the midwife helped manually dilate me from 9.5 to 10 cm. I pushed for a quick 20 minutes before Bodhi arrived, just before 6pm. He did not cry right away, and since there was meconium staining, he was quickly whisked to the other side of the room for suctioning. Bodhi was fine, but this meant no delayed cord clamping—something we had wanted. Bummer. This upset both myself and Rock, but what could we do?

There were a few other instances when the hospital staff challenged our decisions or protocol dictated certain procedures for our outwardly healthy-looking baby. We were exhausted and happy to have Bodhi in our arms but still agitated to have to question, push, and accept things we didn't want. That being said, overall, our experience was a good one, and I am grateful that we had a supportive team of midwives taking care of us. But we had still hoped for better.

Postpartum Round 1

After Bodhi was born and our circle of friends evolved to mostly other parents of young kiddos, we became friends with a few folks that had chosen a home birth for their little ones. As time went on, and we started to think about kiddo number two, we asked more questions of our friends to sus out how we felt about that option. All that we heard from them sounded really appealing. My only concern had been how to handle the mess at home that accompanies birth. My first labor had definitely involved both defecating and vomiting at unexpected times, something I was not looking forward to at home! But our friends assured us that it is all manageable with the help of your homebirth team.

A few other key things happened between Bodhi and baby two. After a series of disappointing jobs, Rock decided to make the bold move to open his own gym. I was very excited to support our family and my husband as he fulfilled a dream. He would be opening a natural movement gym, following the MovNat® methodology. This, of course, also meant that I would never need to pay for a gym membership again, as he had converted me to also be a natural movement enthusiast. I strongly believe that practicing natural movement (e.g., crawling, hanging, balancing, throwing, and more) helped my body in so many ways before and after my first baby, as well as in preparation for baby two. I did struggle with some urinary incontinence after birth and was very glad I had the support of some excellent pelvic floor physical therapists. With their help, combined with MovNat's mindful and deliberate methodology, I felt that, even if I had not fully corrected some dysfunctions, I had the support and tools to fully recover my body after a second birth.

My Home Birth

Considering how uncomplicated the first birth had been, Rock and I easily aligned on a home birth for kiddo number two. That decision was further reinforced when I found out I was pregnant just a few weeks after the COVID-19 pandemic started. Staying out of the overwhelmed hospitals with additional restrictions felt right.

Once I was a little over eight weeks, we looked up a few of the home-birth midwives in our area as well as asked friends for recommendations. We then set up a few virtual consults to get to know our options. It was tough to figure out what questions to ask and how to decide what would be a good fit for us, but after about four different virtual consults, Ingrid Andersson just felt right. The biggest determining factor was her level of engagement with Rock. He and I are very much partners when it comes to the birth and the kids, so when she engaged with him as much as me, that sealed it.

My pregnancy with baby two was a little more challenging compared to my first. I had some of the typical first trimester symptoms like nausea and cramping, and my sense of smell was very strong and opinionated! I had the typical emotional rollercoaster, which exasperated by the chaos in the world, my challenging toddler, and the recent death of my father. I was never sure what to blame for my moodiness since I had many things to pick from.

Other than that, it was another healthy, uneventful pregnancy. Prenatal checkups with Ingrid Andersson and her student, Johanna

Hatch, were wonderful even though we were hiding behind masks. Ingrid had a lovely home office, and we had a whole hour to catch up on all fronts—emotional, physical, and anything else—which really allowed us to develop a strong relationship. Some visits had to be conducted virtually, but that was just fine since we didn't have any major concerns. If it were not for the pandemic, our toddler would have been able to join us to help prepare him for his younger brother. He at least got his own tape measure, thanks to Ingrid, to help measure my belly at home. My care team consisted of Ingrid, Johanna, my pelvic floor physical therapist (something I highly recommend), and those that conducted the procedural visits at the hospital for ultrasounds or specific blood work. We decided not to encapsulate the placenta this time since I had more years under my belt being medication-free and did not want to risk it negatively affecting my milk supply since there is some evidence to support that placenta consumption can do that. I was open to consuming it raw immediately post-delivery to help stop any significant bleeding, but in the end, I did not need it.

Leading up to the birth, we felt as calm and collected as we could. Ingrid and Johanna answered every question we had, and every fear was met with a reassuring response. There was still the stress of trying to keep up with the day to day of family life in a pandemic, but we had all the confidence in our birth team to not feel stress or anxiety about the support they would be providing in bringing our second son into the world. That feeling is priceless.

We went into our 40-week checkup feeling good but anxious to have our baby. I admitted to Ingrid that while I had full confidence in my birthing ability and her support, I was feeling afraid. I had started to really feel the unpredictability of the world around me amid the pandemic and worried about bringing a little person into the world. Ingrid communicated that while it sounded like my body was showing all the right signs it was getting ready for labor and birth, until I was able to get my mind aligned, it could very well keep things from progressing. She suggested that I talk to my baby/belly; that I tell him I was ready for him, that he had a loving home and his parents were waiting for him, and we could not wait to meet him. She told me that sometimes the act of talking aloud would equally help me get past my own fears.

That night, Rock and I both made a point to talk to the baby together. It felt awkward, but I really did not want my mind to get in the way of bringing my baby into this world. I said things like: *We are ready for you. I am ready for you. We will keep you safe. We can't wait to meet you. We are ready when you are.*

At 4:30am the next morning (on my due date), I began to leak amniotic fluid. Apparently, all my baby and mind needed was one reassuring conversation! I was not 100% sure I was leaking amniotic fluid, but I was able to be in constant communication via text message with Ingrid throughout the day for questions or concerns. This was so reassuring. She was able to tell me that everything was normal and that I should expect labor to start within 24 hours. This allowed me to prepare my family and be sure everything was in place, which was not much since we weren't leaving the house! Contractions didn't start to pick up until the late afternoon, and they even decided to slow down to give me just enough bandwidth to help get Bodhi to bed. As soon as Bodhi was securely in his room and on his way to deep sleep, active labor kicked in. My mom and sister arrived shortly after and immediately laid down, just checking in occasionally, knowing this would be a night-time birth. I was so relieved not to have to worry about the right time to head to the hospital. We tracked contractions so we could communicate to Ingrid how things were progressing. A few hours later, Ingrid and Johanna arrived. We waited until things were further along, but Ingrid communicated that she and Johanna would come whenever we wanted them. This, like so much else, was incredibly reassuring.

I labored in a few different positions on the floor in my dimly lit living room and followed Ingrid's advice to try more uncomfortable positions, as they would help move things along faster. "No pain, no gain!" she said. As things moved along, the inflatable birth tub was set up just a few feet away in our dining room. Once it was all set up, I settled into the warm water. And it was glorious! I had not been eligible for a water birth with Bodhi because of my gestation and induction.

Despite the ease and calm, as labor progressed, I realized I was feeling really afraid. I could remember my first birth and the effort and pain of pushing and was afraid I could not do it again. I was afraid of tearing (which I had avoided with Bodhi) and generally of things not going as smoothly as before. I think somehow between contractions I thought to myself—*what's the worst that could happen?* And realized that no matter the answer, I trusted my team and knew they could take care of me. I don't think Forest was ready to come until I got past that fear. My beautiful little boy was born at 2am in the birth tub, just missing his due date. And I was lucky enough to, again, have no tearing. *Thank you, body!* He was placed immediately in my arms, and I will remember those first few moments forever.

Other than the obvious work and excitement of active labor, it was the most peaceful, beautiful birth I could have asked for. And miraculously, Bodhi did not wake up until 4am when we were all getting settled into bed. He made it just in time for a tour of the placenta!

Before Ingrid and Johanna left our house, they did all the necessary clean-up from the birth, including getting laundry started. The best part about the homebirth was not needing to leave the house for the one-day, three-day, and two-week checkups. I could stay in my sweats and breastmilk-soaked clothes without feeling unpresentable.

Ingrid was available by text for all my random questions related to breastfeeding and otherwise. I was surprised how many questions I had, even though this was my second rodeo. I think knowing I had a resource just a text away made all the difference.

Postpartum Round 2

I realize my birth stories may be smoother than some, but no matter what your back story or past birth story is, I simply encourage you to take the time to connect with yourself to determine what feels right for you and your family. There is no right or wrong way—just what is right for you based on the options available.

And be kind to yourself. This is something I am admittedly not very good at. Rock helps me with it every day. I found that the immediate postpartum recovery with Forest to be much harder than I remember it with Bodhi. Seeing Bodhi running around and wanting to spend time with me when what I was able and needed to do was sit, nurse, and rest, just made my heart ache. I felt extremely impatient. I wanted the bleeding to stop right away. I wanted to immediately return to moving and playing with Bodhi how I did before I was even pregnant. These were all unrealistic expectations. There were also some additional ergonomic challenges. Our house is set up for a lot of floor seating, including the dining table. Even our bed is a Japanese-style futon on the floor. This is a result of Rock's passion for movement. This made my impatience worse, as I was not easily able to join the family for dinner sitting on the floor and getting in and out of bed was a challenge at the beginning. Yet, I do believe that our movement focused lifestyle ultimately helped my recovery, as I was accustomed to doing all those things before and throughout pregnancy. And once I was past the first few weeks, I was able to at least move around my house more easily. This helped since we also do all our diaper changes on the floor, and that never ends with a newborn. Believe me, there were many times that I would curse our setup and wish for a changing table or an elevated bed. But without really thinking about it, I had already rebuilt the strength and flexibility to get up and down off the floor countless times a day, and I know my body is better for it.

I was also excited to return to a more formal movement practice that was gentle and supportive of my postpartum body. A great deal changes in our bodies when we do the remarkable work of growing and birthing babies, that we often need to sideline particular movement or fitness goals until we are fully recovered. While I hoped to return to short-distance sprinting and beating my fastest high school mile time, I started with rebuilding my core through breathing and ground-based movements—all of which I was able to incorporate into my daily life with a baby and a toddler.

If you already love what you do for movement/fitness and you can keep it up in pregnancy and beyond, great! If you are interested in something new and live in the Madison area, MovNat Madison is a family and women focused natural movement space where you can move, play, and get strong. You are invited to join our community. If you aren't in the Madison area, connect with us virtually!

I sincerely hope my story helps you in your birthing journey to realize that almost all the time if something doesn't feel quite right, you have the chance to make a different choice. Do what you can to ask questions and educate yourself so you can make the best choice for yourself. Growing, birthing, and raising humans is probably the craziest, most fulfilling work of my life—and gives me strength and purpose when everything else around me gets tough.

ANNE HANCOCK

Anne (Annie) Hancock was born and raised in Northern Virginia. She attended The College of William and Mary ('08), where she earned a B.A. in economics and environmental studies. She also has an M.A. from George Washington University in Organizational Management. She has worked in the non-profit as well as for-profit setting in Washington DC and Madison, WI holding a variety of roles from program coordination to project and program management. She is the mother to two boys, Bodhi and Forest, and currently lives in Madison, WI. In addition to her professional work, she is a MovNat® Certified Trainer and teaches classes at MovNat Madison, a natural movement gym owned and operated by her husband, Rock Hancock. She has a passion for connecting with people on a personal level and helping them improve their day-to-day lives with movement and conversational coaching. When time permits, she loves to run, hike, write poetry, and play – all while spending time with her family.

Additional Info:

Website: www.movnatmadison.com
Email: anne.l.hancock@gmail.com

Facebook: https://www.
facebook.com/movnatmadison/
Instagram: https://www.
instagram.com/movnatmadison/
LinkedIn: https://www.linkedin.com/in/anne-
hancock-599225a/

10

WATERBIRTH: A GLOBAL MOVEMENT TO CHANGE THE WAY WE WELCOME BABIES INTO THE WORLD

BARBARA HARPER, FOUNDER OF WATERBIRTH INTERNNATIONAL

IN MY 32ND week of pregnancy, my obstetrician threatened to have my child taken away from me, screaming that he would report me to the child protective services if I did something so dangerous as to give birth at home, let alone in the water. He turned his chair around and stood up, walked slowly to his bookcase, grabbed a book, slammed it down on his desk, and yelled, "You're one of them! A selfish woman who only wants a "touchy-feely" emotional experience who would risk the life of her baby. Stop this insane nonsense right now." I picked up the book and read the cover. It was titled "Immaculate Deception" by Suzanne Arms. I asked the doctor if I could borrow it.

That was late summer of 1984. I started planning a home waterbirth with a local nurse who had a good reputation as a midwife. A month before having this confrontation with my obstetrician, my partner and I had taken a trip to France for my 33rd birthday. I wanted to find the hospital, an hour outside of Paris, that offered warm water immersion as a comfort measure during labor and where women could birth in the big pools, too. I had heard about this from several different sources and felt like I was on a research quest. Dr. Michel Odent was the physician and obstetric consultant for the midwives at the Hospital Generale in Pithiviers, France. He published an article in the Lancet in December 1983, detailing his experience with 100 cases of birth in water.[1] The only other article that I could find when I started searching for information about this method at the UCLA medical library was from a French medical journal with a publication date of 1805.[2] I also saw an article in a magazine that showed photos of glass tanks in the Soviet Union with babies swimming, dangling between the legs of women, suspended by their umbilical cords. I had always dismissed anything that was printed in this sensational magazine, The National Enquirer. These photos and the article were just odd enough for me to introduce the idea to my partner.

We had discussed making a baby, and he immediately wanted to go to Russia to give birth, where his parents had been born. I suggested we simply stay at home and study about it before we launched into something I was not so sure about. Let's talk to the midwife and see if she knows anything about waterbirth.

I was a pediatric nurse specialist who had graduated with honors from nursing school a decade before. I also had achieved specialties in cardiac intensive care and neurosurgical intensive care. I literally had spent my entire life in hospitals, as my grandmother was the director of patient care in a rural hospital in Ohio and throughout her life had attended hundreds of births at home. She was the one who urged me to go into nursing. I loved being a nurse, and I also loved babies and maternity care. However, my love of mothers and babies did not do well in the hospital in my early career. I worked in labor and delivery and was very quickly asked to leave. I was constantly getting into trouble for putting mothers and babies back together, encouraging mothers to breastfeed, and refusing to give mothers sleeping pills after birth. The worst reprimand came after reporting a physician for sexual abuse of more than one patient. The details are not important. It happened, and I felt obligated to the women to prevent it from continuing. He did continue the abuse for another 10 years. I, however, was asked to leave and transferred into intensive care. I always felt like I had to get back to the babies.

The first woman that I helped set up a waterbirth was a mother of five children, pregnant with her sixth baby whom I met in my pediatric practice. She is the person who gave me the National Enquirer magazine that ended up changing my entire life path. I helped her plan her birth by purchasing all the equipment – a kiddie pool from Sears, the hoses, a floating pool thermometer, and a tarp for the floor. I was so excited for her. On the night she had her baby in February 1984, I stayed home, too afraid to attend the birth, even though she asked me to. Midwifery, outside of the hospital in California during that time, was not exactly supported or advertised. It happened. You had to be incredibly careful if you were a midwife. No one could admit they were attending home births, especially nurses. They could have their license taken away. Midwives stayed under the medical radar. I stayed up all night waiting for the mother to call to let me know how it went. My partner stayed up with me, and we ended up distracting ourselves by making a baby.

I went into full research mode and wrote letters to anyone that I heard possibly knew anything about waterbirth. I also went to the anthropology library at UCLA and found references to laboring in water by indigenous cultures around the world. Now, I was in France, hoping that I could also find Dr. Frederick Leboyer. His 1975 book, "Birth Without Violence,"[3] had also changed my life.

I already gave birth to a daughter in 1978 and prepared while working in the same hospital for an unmedicated birth in a new "birthing room" where my husband could be present. From my previous labor and delivery experience as a nurse, I knew exactly what I did not want. Leboyer's book emboldened me to ask for low lights, soft voices, a warm bath for the baby after birth to encourage relaxation and to simulate being back in the womb. This was a practice already present in many American hospitals – putting the baby into warm water right after birth. They called it the Leboyer bath. It made such sense for the baby to relax and recover from birth, knowing that the way we birth babies affects how their brains wire for either connection, peace, and love or shock and fear. I wanted to hold my baby immediately and tell her how much she was wanted.

The birthing room turned out to be a cold, sterile delivery room with a lounge chair for the husband. I was strapped down to a hard metal table with hands in leather restraints and not allowed to move, episiotomy cut against my pleas not to do it, Demerol injected without my consent, which made me nauseous, vomiting, dizzy, and out of control, and my baby was whisked off to the nursery and not allowed to be returned to me for the next 15 hours. Hospital policy required an examination by the pediatrician of record before the baby could be released into the mother's care. I gave birth on a Sunday evening, and my pediatrician was not making rounds until Monday afternoon. I swore I would never have sex again so I would not have to give birth in a hospital. Well, that did not work. However, I did divorce that husband.

Pregnant with partner number two, who totally supported my research into waterbirth, we found ourselves in Paris looking for Dr. Leboyer. I was fortunate enough to be introduced to him, and we had a wonderful discussion about gentle birth and warm water immersion. He was not so much in favor of birth in water, but he sent me to the hospital in Paris, where tubs had been installed, and I attended a childbirth class there. My poor 17-year-old male French interpreter who faithfully translated female reproductive anatomy and physiology was convinced he would never engage in sexual activity that could produce a pregnancy until he was married if that is what a woman had to go through after a few minutes of sexual pleasure. The built-in pools at this hospital were plain. The birth rooms were unadorned, with only rocking chairs and small beds. No monitors, no harsh lights, tall windows that could open or be shuttered to keep out the light. When I inquired if any mother actually gave birth in the water, the midwives laughed and assured me that they were too small in weight compared to a pregnant laboring mother to haul her out of the water if the baby was coming. Yes, they caught many babies in the water at this hospital. I heard the exact same response to my question at the hospital where the women in Dr. Odent's Lancet article had given birth. The difference between the two facilities was the celebration of birth in water that appeared in the large meeting room at the hospital in Pithivier. The walls were covered with photographs of women giving birth in the water, on the floor, squatting, supported by their partners' strong arms suspending them in a squatting position. Birth photos showed mothers holding their babies in the water after birth, kissing them, exploring them, nursing them. I was overwhelmed and completely in tears viewing this magnificent photo montage. What was it that made birth here in a small country hospital in France so different from birth in any hospital in America?

The answer was amazingly simple. The environment of the rooms in France were home-like. Dr. Odent, in his 1986 book, "Birth Reborn,"[4] talked about some of the same things that Dr. Leboyer had described in his more poetic Birth Without Violence book. Odent wrote that birth is instinctive. An environment that promotes intimacy and free expression are essential in the experience of birth. The role of the midwife must be key to the mother's experience. Low lights, autonomy, freedom to move, warm baths, different positions for birth which allow the pelvis to open and baby to be born quickly without an episiotomy, with midwives offering nurturing touch, gentleness, and loving care for both mother and baby. That was my answer. The only way I could have that type of experience was at home. I did not know of a single hospital that I had worked in or heard of where women were "allowed" to birth freely.

While in Pithivier, I asked to see a birth in water, and my request was immediately denied. Out came my nursing license, my Red Cross CPR card, and my American Nurses Association membership card, all in an effort to convince this midwife that I was totally qualified to be at a birth. She explained that I was a stranger to the mother, and my presence in the room, no matter how skilled I was at resuscitating babies, would disturb the mother's energy. I cried and then sobbed. Finally, she relented and asked the mother if I could watch, warning me that there was to be no eye contact with the mother and to keep my distance. I sat in the corner of the room and watched the mother move freely in the water, moan softly and then suddenly get out of the water and squat with her partner's help close to the floor. The midwife spread a clean sheet on the floor and sat down, legs crossed, no gloves, no equipment, and waited while the mother grunted, breathed, opened her throat, and sang her baby down into the waiting hands of the midwife. The baby was placed onto the sheet, and the mother lowered herself down to sit, legs spread on either side of her newborn. She started petting the baby's back, and as she did, the baby started mewing softly like a newly born kitten, and that is when the mother picked up the baby, and they looked each other in the eyes. The memory of what birth could be was indelibly etched into my brain that day.

I had gone to my obstetrician for a regular prenatal visit a few weeks after my visit to France and was excited to tell him about meeting Dr. Leboyer and touring the two hospitals. That's when the threats came. I dug my heels in and planned my home birth without telling my doctor. I figured if anything happened to cause me to need an obstetrician, it was better to lie to him and keep him thinking I was going to show up at the hospital.

Just Add Water....

My second birth was so good, so successful, so incredible, in a hand-built water tub at the end of my bed, with Pachelbel playing, candles as the only light, and flowers everywhere. My baby slid out like a slippery dolphin, no perineal tearing, and I turned to my midwife and told her right then that I needed to tell every woman on the planet how easy birth could be. I also called my doctor's office the next morning and said that the baby had been born at home, in water, and to tell the doctor kindly he could go fuck himself. That probably was not the right thing to say, but I just could not help myself. A few weeks later, he followed through on his threat, and two investigators from the county Child Protective Services knocked on my door. I told them the entire story about the French tour, showed them the National Enquirer, gave them a copy of Dr. Odent's article, and described my birth. The woman investigator asked me for a glass of water and followed me into the kitchen. There, she whispered that she was newly pregnant and would love to have a waterbirth. I told her to come back after the case was dropped.

I started sharing my experience of waterbirth with anyone who would listen. Even ABC news was interested. I was on a few talk shows and taught a professional workshop for nurses, midwives, and doctors in my living room. Another personal waterbirth in 1986, and the 15 babies that had been born in water in my house, convinced me that I needed to start studying to be a midwife. By 1988, I had founded the only nonprofit organization to provide accurate information on using warm water immersion for labor and birth. I connected with other women who had given birth in water in different parts of the planet, and Waterbirth International suddenly was receiving requests from all over the US and the world.

The packets of information that we mailed out to thousands of couples simply stated the benefits, contained copies of articles, including the 1983 Lancet article, and gave women the option to rent a portable pool for their birth. There was huge resistance from both the obstetric community and the midwifery community in the beginning. Midwives said, "if we were meant to give birth in water, our babies would be born with gills." Education about the normal physiologic processes that take place during birth, switching the fetus from receiving oxygen from the placenta via the umbilical cord to an air-breathing, gas exchanging newborn was paramount. Supporting the retrospective collection of data was difficult in the US, but in the UK, teams of researchers from the late 80s onwards established national databases to collect, collate, and review raw data from thousands of water labors and births in hospitals, birth centers, and homes.

By 1995 we had not heard anything from the American College of Obstetricians and Gynecologists (ACOG) about waterbirth. Directly asking their opinion of the use of warm water immersion for labor AND birth, I sent a letter accompanied with a three-ring binder containing all the published peer-reviewed scientific journal articles from the UK, Europe, and a few case studies in the US. Hoping that one of the articles by Dr. Michael Rosenthal, a fellow of ACOG, who was the first obstetrician in the US to open a free-standing birth center in Upland, California, would impress them.[5] They did write back and stated that until there were randomized controlled studies with populations of 10,000 or more women published in peer-reviewed journals within the United States, that they would never have an opinion. They admitted it was an intriguing subject, and please update them when those studies were published.

Our evidence was thousands of healthy babies and mothers who loved their experience using water, with 100 percent of them saying they would seek the experience again if given the opportunity. One woman on her paper survey wrote across the back, "Would not have another waterbirth. This is number seven. I'm DONE." The first hospital in the US to offer waterbirth in 1991 was in the small town of Peterborough, New Hampshire. A midwife from the UK had relocated there and helped them start a waterbirth program that is still operating today in Monadnock Community Hospital. Waterbirth in America first spread through the home birth midwifery community. Waterbirth International offered conferences and training for any midwife, doctor, or nurse. We organized a few international conferences in 1996, 2000, 2004, 2007, and continued teaching workshops at midwifery conventions and within hospitals across North America. We started teaching in China in 2005 and have been in China every year since then.

The current estimated number of US hospitals offering water immersion as an option for both labor and birth is just under fifteen percent of all maternity care facilities. Women in the US and around the world are seeking a kinder, gentler way to birth their babies.

Many women are not just looking for pain relief but a way to remain drug-free, relaxed, and with some control over the process of letting the baby out. Couples may have read about the impact of early childhood trauma, including birth trauma, on the developmental neurobiology, endocrinology, immunology, microbiome, and epigenetics of this new human being. Women do not want to recover from post-traumatic stress after birth or deal with post-partum depression, which is much more prevalent when women are not included in the decision-making process.[6] Over the past four decades, I have personally observed over one thousand women in birth pools, listened carefully, and recorded many actions and characteristics in mothers, babies, and their caregivers. I have heard many caregivers and mothers retell their stories to friends, family, and to their babies. Women often use the same words to describe how their babies responded after birth and in the months and years that followed. Is it just the water that caused these babies to be alert, calm, responsive, connected, present, and aware? The use of warm water immersion aids and assists the mother in feeling calm, relaxed, nurtured, protected, in control with the ability to easily move as her body and her baby dictate. From the mother's perspective, using water becomes the best way to enhance the natural process without any evidence of increased risk. A calm, relaxed mother is more likely to experience a calm, relaxed baby after birth.

The goal of pediatricians and obstetricians who object to waterbirth with concerns about the baby and the goal of mothers who choose undisturbed birth is really exactly the same. They are both thinking of the baby and what the baby needs to enhance its quality of life from the very beginning.

A joint meeting of the Royal College of Obstetricians, the Royal College of Midwives, and the National Childbirth Trust in 2006, examined many different birthing methods and modalities. Their main question was, "what would increase the normalcy of birth without increasing risk?" and the very first agreement that went into a joint statement was that access to water for labor and birth would accomplish that objective, so..... Just Add Water.[7] We knew there was no turning back after that statement was released.

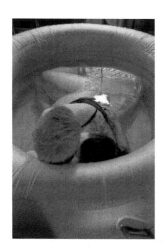

What Keeps a Baby Safe During a Waterbirth?

Belief in the safety of waterbirth comes with a complete understanding of the mechanisms which prevent the baby from inhaling or gasping while it is still submerged in the water, as the head is born, and after the full body has slipped into the water. One must also possess knowledge of the triggers for newborn breathing and what takes place in the cardiovascular system as the baby transitions from fetal circulation to newborn circulation. The fear of aspiration is a strong deterrent to waterbirth for some providers and a grave concern for pediatricians and parents alike.

When a baby is born, everyone awaits that first cry which signals that the newborn has emerged safely from the womb. Even a slight delay of that response is incredibly stressful for most people. Others view the newly born baby in the water opening his eyes and stretching his limbs in awe, and see a baby who is doing exactly what he did for nine months in the womb. Those babies stretching and opening their eyes are still completely supported by placental circulation but now are in a larger expanded womb, the water of the birth pool – a womb with a view. It is an absolute miracle to witness this "in-between" worlds after the baby emerges into the water as if everything is in slow motion. Someone, whether mother, father, midwife, doctor, reaches down and lifts the baby up and into the mother's waiting arms. No need to rush; the baby is safe and cannot physiologically attempt to take a breath while still in the water. Mother's often need a minute to come back into the present moment and realize the baby is out.

There are two important triggers for initiating the process that allows the newborn to take his first breath. The first is the presence of nitrogen in room air. We usually think that oxygen is the trigger; however, our atmosphere is made up of 78 percent nitrogen and only 21 percent oxygen. The newborn's face has receptors that interpret the presence of nitrogen and presence of gravity, which is the second trigger. Gravity is pushing equally on the face and stimulating the trigeminal nerve (the fifth cranial nerve) receptor areas around the nose and mouth. Human beings need the force of 14.7 pounds per square inch of gravity, as well as the presence of nitrogen molecules to trigger the switch from being a fetus supported by the placenta to being a newborn who is able to breathe in oxygen and breathe out carbon dioxide.

In the womb, the fetus receives oxygen only through the placenta. The fetal heart shunts or bypasses the lungs, liver, and skin, only sending oxygenated blood where it is needed most. The arrival into room air is interpreted by the receptors on the face, which signals the entire system to change quickly. The shunting system with openings in the heart to bypass the lungs and the liver are chemically ordered to close. Once the openings in the heart – the shunts (the foramen ovale and ductus arteriosus) close and highly oxygenated blood flows into the pulmonary arteries, the well-vascularized tissue around the air sacs (alveoli) quickly fill the capillaries that surround the air sac. This sac looks like a deflated balloon and is filled with fluid. All this fluid is quickly pulled into the capillaries that are now engorged with blood just for this purpose. This thick viscous fluid that was present in the lungs during fetal life will now increase the blood volume by as much as 20 percent.[8] The sacs (alveoli) can now begin to exchange oxygen and carbon dioxide. The necessity to breathe is not a lack of oxygen. It is a build-up of carbon dioxide – it must be discharged first.

Immediately after birth, the cardiac output to the lung must increase from the 8 percent level during fetal life to a 55 percent level necessary for neonatal transition and breathing for the rest of this human being's life. Therefore, some of the blood from the placenta, which acted as the fetal lung, is now needed by the actual neonatal lung for opening all 50 million individual lung cells. Keeping the blood pumping from the placenta after birth is vitally important to increase the vitality and health of this newly functioning little human. When the cord is cut within the first one to two minutes, especially after a waterbirth, the many benefits of placental transfusion are lost forever, and this compromises lung expansion and function.[9] The infant is left with only the blood that was in the body at the time of cord clamping, which is not adequate to create an increase in the circulatory bed while the infant's organs (lung, liver, kidney, skin, gut, and brain) begin to assume the functions sustained by the placenta during fetal life. In other words, the more blood that flows from the placenta into the newborn, the higher the blood volume. The more blood volume and the thicker the blood, the more fluids can leave the lung tissue.[10]

Some of the mechanisms that function to switch the newborn from fetal circulation to newborn status take place over the course of hours and sometimes days. Not all the fluids that were in the lungs prenatally are pulled out into the vascular circulation. The fluids that remain are drawn out of the lung cells through the lymphatic system, which is stimulated over the following 72 hours by skin-to-skin placement, self-attachment, and breastfeeding.[11] One of the many benefits of waterbirth for both mother and newborn is the immediate placement of the baby against the mother's chest with uninterrupted skin-to-skin contact. Waterbirth providers have learned so much from observing what normal full-term healthy newborns do in the sanctuary of the mother's chest, between the breasts. The neonate who is placed skin-to-skin regulates all his systems very quickly and is often extremely quiet.[12] The absence of vigorous crying is not indicative of the absence of newborn breathing. Quiet, stable newborn breathing often happens without a single peep out of the baby, who is immediately placed on the mother's chest. This has been a frequent observation of babies who are born in water.

Whether born on land or in the water, all babies stop their outward progression after the head is born before the shoulders come. The innate reflex requires that the baby wait for the peak of the next contraction when the force of the contraction allows the pelvic floor muscles to rotate the shoulders of the baby. The bottom of the baby's feet are stimulated by the contraction from the top of the uterus pushing downward, giving him a foot massage, which causes him to simply eject himself out of the birth canal. As the baby waits for the next contraction with its head out, the baby who is born on land begins the process of switching from fetal placenta-supported circulation to newborn circulation. The baby who is born in water, and for that matter, a baby born in the breech position, only begins to transition into the newborn state, switching the circulation system, when the head meets the air for the first time.

No other part of the body will trigger the switch from fetal circulation to newborn circulation. While the baby is still in the water, you can touch the head, hold a hand, grab any part, and it will not stimulate the baby to switch his system. That baby needs room air and gravity, neither of which are present in the water. When researchers compare Apgar scores between land born babies and water babies, the result, the water baby is usually slightly lower. It takes a few more seconds for the baby who is born in water to catch up. Water babies tend to have a slightly lower one-minute Apgar score, but the five-minute evaluation is very often much higher when compared to bed births.[13] This is easily attributed to the fact that in all waterbirths, it is suggested to leave the umbilical cord alone while the cord continues to pulse and even better is to wait until the placenta is birthed before separating the baby from the placenta by cutting the cord. The physiologic third stage is common practice during a waterbirth and not so common practice in hospitals around the world. An experienced and well-educated provider will be more of a lifeguard, not interfering with the natural process unless absolutely necessary.

The Solution to Pollution is Dilution

Water immersion for labor and water assisted birth never stopped during the pandemic in many places around the world. Too many women had benefited from the use of water to warrant suspension of the practice. The US was one of the more cautious places. Yet, there were many hospitals that continued waterbirth and adjusted their use of personal protective equipment, covid testing, and limitations on people who could accompany birthing women.

Safety concerns about waterbirth and COVID-19 were first raised in March 2020 by a joint paper from the RCM and RCOG revealing research that the virus had been found in feces. This led to a statement suggesting water use should stop due to fear of fecal contamination. This took everyone by surprise, and our email was soon full of messages from midwives and doctors who support the use of water in labor and saw no reason to stop even with contaminated feces in the water. After all, the solution to pollution is dilution. Waterbirth International addressed these concerns early in 2020 with a blog post and video that is still on our website.

Covid is not a waterborne virus. It has been confirmed to be transmitted through air, via droplets from coughing, sneezing, or breathing. Immersing in warm water during labour and/or birth is not likely to increase the risk of transmission; instead, it may reduce the risk of transmission.

Hospitals, as well as home birth practitioners, asked about adding something to the water to "kill" the virus. Tap water in most countries is chlorinated, which will likely stop all bacterial and viral infections. There have been no known or recorded cases of the virus being transmitted via feces and no recorded cases of oral-fecal transmission. The Centers for Disease Control and Prevention (CDC) states: "There is no evidence that COVID-19 can be spread to humans using pools or hot tubs. Proper operation, maintenance, and disinfection of pools and hot tubs should remove or inactivate the virus that causes COVID-19." needs a foot-note - unless you are willing to let it go.[14]

Yes, some women will poop during birth wherever they happen to be. Women using water are encouraged to follow their bodies and only push at the peak of the contraction with a little effort, breathing the baby down and singing the baby through the pelvis. Huge bearing down, breath-holding, counting through the contraction efforts are discouraged or not used at all.[15] The position that the mother assumes, the patience of waiting for the shoulders, and not forcing women to push just because the cervix is fully open helps mitigate the excretion of fecal matter, and it also helps keep the perineal tissue intact.[16]

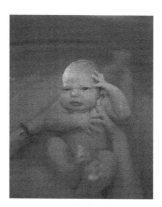

Arranging for a waterbirth – essential knowledge

Waterbirth is an option for birth all over the world. World-renowned hospitals, as well as small community hospitals and birthing centers, offer waterbirth as an option to low-risk clients. Today there are many studies, including the Cochrane Library of Systematic Reviews, that find overwhelming data supporting the safety and efficacy of water-birth for both mothers and their babies.[17]

Both the caregiver attending a waterbirth and the mother giving birth must possess confidence and trust in the process of birth in water. Two more recent studies highlighted that birth in water is safe out of the hospital environment. Water use was just one part of The Midwives Alliance of North America data collection from members who attend births at home and in midwife owned birth centers. In data that was collected from 2005 to 2009, almost 17,000 births were reported, with 34 percent taking place in water, including 13 sets of twins born at home.[18] Planned home birth is reasonable, safe, economical, and many women will use a pool to assist with labor and birth.

Another out-of-hospital study with comparable results was published in March 2020, reviewing the data from over 26,000 births in community settings, both free-standing birth centers, and home, where there are no monitors, epidurals, or narcotics given to laboring women.[19] However, most birth centers, as reported by the American Association of Birth Centers, offer the use of hydrotherapy to increase comfort in labor. Women, in almost every birth center, may stay in the water to birth their babies. In this study, 38 percent gave birth in water, which makes it more than 10,000 women in one study that ACOG was looking for in 1995. The AABC study concludes that "personal preferences should drive utilization of care practices, rather than professional preferences or institutionalized restrictions, which limit access to safe childbearing options for women." That statement is exactly why women started looking for safe and reasonable options outside of hospitals. Access to water has been limited in institutionalized birth, and many women feel like they must fight to receive the care that they desire.

Waterbirth is safe for women who have experienced a healthy pregnancy and are anticipating a non-complicated physiologic birth. Within that definition, there is some judgement about what physiologic and non-complicated means. Some midwives will define it as normal physiology with acceptable variations. Here are some of the acceptable variations of normal physiology.

- Vaginal birth after previous cesarean birth
- Twins
- Breech position of the fetus
- Group Beta Strep positive mother

- Rh negative mothers
- Grand multiparous women – more than five previous births
- Babies that are expected to weigh more than 4.5 kilograms (9 pounds)
- Women who have a BMI (Body Mass Index) of greater than 30
- Gestational Diabetes controlled by diet

The key to being able to use the water with one or more of these complexities is to find a midwife with experience in handling those specific cases. With or without water, VBAC, twins, and breech positions can all be birthed vaginally with an experienced and confident provider.

When a woman emails or calls me and asks if I can assist her in getting her hospital to offer waterbirth, the first question I ask is, "how pregnant are you?"

We need at least six months to accomplish that task. The next question I ask is, "Have you explored the option of home birth in your area? I'm happy to help you find a referral."

Women have been successful in advocating for changes in hospitals. That process requires a persistent mother, a willing provider, and a hard-working and cooperative nurse manager in the labor and delivery or women's healthcare department. The mother needs to follow up diligently. The provider must be willing and able to work with different committees and departments and seek education or even certification. Waterbirth International specializes in this process and has helped many hospitals around the world introduce the use of water for labor and birth. I have personally taught workshops in 75 countries. The nurse manager is usually the most important person because that person coordinates the meetings, writes the policies, attends all the meetings of each committee, and supervises the training of the nursing staff. There are now more Waterbirth Education Community Doulas around the US since we introduced that program in 2020. They have been trained to assist mothers in navigating the system, and they are also excellent resources for referrals to birth centers and home birth midwives.

Getting the right equipment for your home birth use of water has never been easier. The night my son was born in the hand-made tub at the foot of the bed, the tub collapsed while my midwife was checking me for tears, and my partner was still in the water holding the baby. 300 gallons (1135 liters) of bloody water spilled onto my bedroom floor and up the walls in a sudden tsunami. I also told my midwife that night that I had to create the perfect birth pool. My second waterbirth was in an outdoor hot tub – not the best choice for a birth, but manageable with my midwife inside the tub with me. I was very vocal during that birth. The neighbors were putting on a new roof that beautiful sunny and warm November afternoon. Every contraction for the last hour of my four-hour labor was spent moaning, sounding rather... shall we say... sexual...orgasmic.

"Oh baby, yes, yes, yes!!! That's it!! You're coming!! I can feel you!!

To the point that one of the work crew came to the door and asked if I needed privacy. My helper told them I was having a baby in the hot tub. From that point on, all the hammering stopped during the contractions. When the lusty cries of my 10-pound baby boy wafted through the air, there was shouting and clapping from the workers.

There has been a great deal of conscious effort, planning, design, and manufacturing to produce the perfect inflatable birth pools for home, birth center, and hospital use. Many companies distribute them. Waterbirth International rented portable pools for many years until we found that the new inflatables were much more economical, easier to set up, and less expensive to purchase than even a rental pool. What do you do with it after you are finished using the birth pool?

Upcycle to your friends who are having a baby – all you need is a new liner.

Or you can save it for your next baby, and use it for early infant swimming lessons, too. They also make a safe place for baby naps.

If you order a pool for only your use, you do not need a liner. Most of the companies include a disposable liner in the kit that comes with everything else you need to fill, drain, monitor the temperature, and hook up your hose to your faucet or shower.

Do not fill the tub in advance of labor. You can go through a test run to see how long it takes, then drain and leave it empty until you are ready to use it. Never leave a pool sitting with water in it for longer than 24 hours. First, the water will cool off. Second, the water will breed bacteria. Under normal use, you fill the portable pool with tap water and use it right away. The temperature should be comfortable for the mother, between 92-97 Fahrenheit (32-37C). You want the temperature to be close to skin temperature, not body temperature. Your skin maintains a temperature of 92-96F (32-36C) and warmer temperatures drain your energy by overheating your system. If you get overheated, your baby gets overheated and will let us know by increasing the heart rate into what is known as tachycardia. It is not dangerous, but it stresses the baby's system. If that happens, get out of the water, cool it down, and get in again. Be sure to drink lots of fluids during your labor, especially while laboring in water. A good rule of thumb is 500ml an hour – that is one regular size water bottle.

Water creates a physical reaction in the body. Deep immersion provides warmth and buoyancy, which reduces muscle tension and lessens anxiety. Even a shower stimulating your skin fibers will decrease your catecholamine level and increase your natural oxytocin, the hormone that is responsible for making the contractions strong. Water is CPR® for labor – it creates comfort, peace, and relaxation. Many women are tense and full of normal anxiety, especially in a first-time birthing person. The fear leads to more tension, and more tension makes the contractions more painful. Water interrupts that cycle. Water is the bridge that creates a deep and profound way to relax. When the body is relaxed, the muscles work much more efficiently. Providers who have not seen very many waterbirths, often say the mother looks "too relaxed," implying that the labor is not progressing. The uterus is doing the work; the mother just is not responding in the same way when she is on the bed.

Providers who practice "masterly inactivity" find that the right time for women to get into the water is when the mother decides she needs more support.

The conscious awareness of the progression of labor within the body, tuning into the rhythm of the contractions and the movements of the baby, is more easily achieved in the water. The option to get in early is up to the mother. One of two things will happen. You will relax so much; the labor will progress more quickly. Or you will relax so much; the labor may slow down. I usually witness the former – the CPR® effect happens, and labor progresses more quickly.

Consciousness is a relatively new study within neuroscience and psychology. There are programs and departments in universities throughout the world studying the effects of mindfulness meditation on the ability to change brain pathways and to even forge new ones.[20] The use of medical hypnosis and programs like Blissborn Birth Hypnosis® have added another interesting element to the birth room. The baby is a conscious participant in his birth. Babies are always listening, responding to their internal environment, and expressing their neurological system to prepare for life outside the womb. The baby is not the passenger during birth—the baby is the driver! This baby has a pre-programmed neurobehavior and a biological imperative to leave the womb – to get out. The fetus is going to accomplish this task much more easily when the mother is profoundly relaxed. The combination of water and self-hypnosis training creates births where the mother surrenders to the power of the energy of creation within the safety of this special environment, surrounded by loved ones, immersed in water, and letting the baby do what it needs to do, letting the baby out. We call this undisturbed birth.

Parting thoughts...

German philosopher Arthur Schopenhauer (1788-1860) is quoted as saying, "All truth passes through three stages. First, it is ridiculed. Second, it is violently opposed. Third, it is accepted as being self-evident." In some parts of the US, the benefits of waterbirth are accepted as self-evident, and it is promoted as being easier for mothers and better for babies. In other places, waterbirth is still being questioned. And in some places, waterbirth and home birth are still being violently opposed by those who do not understand all the benefits that undisturbed birth provides for both mother and baby. Couples want safe, satisfying births where the provider attends as a powerful guardian of the experience, trusting the woman and her baby to unfold at their own pace in their own way, including the use of water throughout the birth process. My mission statement for Waterbirth International is, "We ensure that waterbirth is an available option for all women in all birth settings." It may not happen during my lifetime, and I knew that from the beginning in 1984, when I made the commitment to tell every woman on the planet how easy birth can be when you just add water. I start my 70th year in June 2021, and I do hope that I am blessed with another 20 years of working on my mission in life – to change the way we welcome babies into the world. My hope is also that the next generation will be vocal in asking for what they want and need to achieve an easy, comfortable, relaxed, and peaceful birth experience.

1. Odent, M. Birth under water. Lancet 1983: 1476-1477
2. Embry M (1805) Observations sur un accouchement terminedans le bain. Ann Soc Med Pract Montp 53:185–191
3. Leboyer, F. Birth Without Violence, Knopf 1975
4. Odent, M. Birth Reborn, Pantheon 1986
5. Rosenthal, M. Warm-water immersion in labor and birth. The Female Patient, 1991 16, 35-46.
6. Slater, P. M. "Post-Traumatic Stress Disorder Managed Successfully with Hypnosis and the Rewind Technique: Two Cases in Obstetric Patients." International Journal of Obstetric Anesthesia, vol. 24, no. 3, Aug. 2015, pp. 272–75, doi:10.1016/j.ijoa.2015.03.003.
7. Alfirevic Z, Gould D. Immersion in water during labour and birth (RCOG/Royal College of Midwives joint statement no. 1). http://www.rcog.org.uk/womens-health/clinical-guidance/immersion-water-during-labour-and-birth. Published January 4, 2006
8. Johnson P. Birth under water: to breathe or not to breathe. Br J Obstet Gynaecol.1996;103:202-8.
9. Mercer JS, Skovgaard RI. Neonatal transition physiology: a new paradigm. J Perinatal Neonatal Nursing (2002) 15(4)56-75
10. Mercer,JS., Vohr, BR., Erickson-Owens,DA., Padbury, JF., and Oh, W. Seven-month developmental outcomes of very low birth weight infants enrolled in a randomized controlled trial of delayed versus immediate cord clamping. Journal of Perinatology (2010) 30, 11–16
11. Moore, E. R., Anderson, G. C., & Bergman, N. (2007). Early skin-to-skin contact for mothers and their healthy newborn infants. Cochrane Database of Systematic Reviews, (3), CD003519.

12. Mori, R., Khanna, R., Pledge, D., & Nakayama T. (2010). A meta-analysis of physiological effects of skin-to-skin contact for newborns and mothers. Pediatrics International, 52(2), 161–170

13. Vanderlaan, Jennifer, et al. "Neonatal Outcomes with Water Birth: A Systematic Review and Meta-Analysis." Midwifery, vol. 59, 2018, pp. 27–38, doi:10.1016/j.midw.2017.12.023.

14. "Municipal Water and COVID-19." Centers for Disease Control and Prevention, Centers for Disease Control and Prevention, 10 Mar 2020, www.cdc.gov/coronavirus/2019-ncov/php/water.html. Accessed 25 April 2021

15. Bosomworth A and Bettany-Saltikov J (2006). 'Just take a deep breath: a review to compare the effects of spontaneous versus directed Valsalva pushing in the second stage of labour on maternal and fetal well- being'. MIDIRS Midwif Dig, 16(2): 157-165.

16. Lemos, A. et al. Coch Data Sys Rev (2017) Pushing/bearing down methods for the second stage of labour. https://doi.org/10.1002/14651858.CD009124.pub3 Accessed Oct. 21, 2020

17. Cluett, Elizabeth R., et al. "Immersion in Water during Labour and Birth." Cochrane Database of Systematic Reviews, no. 5, 2018, doi:10.1002/14651858.CD000111.pub4.

18. Bovbjerg, Marit L., Cheyney, M., Everson, C. (2016) "Maternal and Newborn Outcomes Following Waterbirth: The Midwives Alliance of North America Statistics Project, 2004 to 2009 Cohort." Journal of Midwifery & Women's Health 61 (1): 11–20

19. Cluett, Elizabeth R., et al. "Immersion in Water during Labour and Birth." Cochrane Database of Systematic Reviews, no. 5, 2018, doi:10.1002/14651858.CD000111.pub4.

20. Downe, S., et al. "Self-Hypnosis for Intrapartum Pain Management in Pregnant Nulliparous Women: A Randomised Controlled Trial of Clinical Effectiveness." BJOG: An International Journal of Obstetrics & Gynaecology, vol. 122, no. 9, 2015, pp. 1226–34, doi:10.1111/1471-0528.13433.

BARBARA HARPER

Barbara Harper is an internationally recognized expert on waterbirth and gentle birth, a published author who founded the non-profit organization, Waterbirth International, in 1988, with one goal in mind – to ensure that waterbirth is an "available option" for all women. During the past five decades Barbara has worked as an obstetric, pediatric, and critical care nurse, midwife, midwifery instructor, childbirth educator, and Blissborn Hypnosis teacher/trainer. She teaches unique seminars within hospitals, nursing schools, midwifery and medical schools and community groups worldwide. Her bestselling book, 'Gentle Birth Choices,' has been translated into 9 languages, including Chinese. Known for her award-winning website and online Waterbirth Certification Courses, Barbara has spent her Covid time researching and writing two new books. Expect The Essential Guide to Waterbirth and Gentle Birth Wisdom, soon. She is the mother of three adult children and two grandsons. She lives in Boca Raton, Florida.

Website: www.waterbirth.org
Twitter @waterbirth
Instagram:

@waterbirthint
@thebarbaraharper

11

FREEBIRTH AFTER HOSPITAL BIRTH

ALIA WRIGHT

My name is Alia Wright. I am a former doula, now a more traditional birth attendant. I am a stay-at-home mom of 2, and these are my stories.

I was just 17 when I found out I was pregnant with my first son, Sammy. I wasn't scared or even surprised. I was able to finish high school early and work full time throughout my pregnancy to save up money for the new baby. My mother was supportive, and I would still be able to start attending college one month after he was born. When I told the school guidance counselor about my pregnancy to figure out my options for finishing school and keeping my scholarships, she informed me of a non-profit organization that worked with teen moms. Through this organization, I was assigned a caseworker who visited me a few times a month to teach me about pregnancy, birth, newborn care, and parenting skills. I watched a show throughout my pregnancy all about birth stories and was excited to have my baby. I never knew home birth was even an option at this point.

I had an overall easy and healthy pregnancy, but at 34 weeks, I went into preterm labor. The day before my graduation ceremony, I had been looking forward to participating in, and we had rehearsal. Through the rehearsal, I went up and down several flights of stairs several times and left feeling quite exhausted. That evening I began to have powerful contractions, so I went to the hospital. I learned that I was in preterm labor (3cm dilated), and I was told I would be given two medications—one to help my baby's lungs develop and another that would try to stop the contractions. While the medication I was given to stop the contractions worked, it also gave me extreme chest pain. When I reported the pains to my medical team, they told me I would need to see a cardiologist to make sure everything was ok for me to go home. Well, the cardiologist at that hospital wouldn't see me because I was under 18, and there was no pediatric cardiologist on staff. I had to be transferred to the children's hospital to have my heart looked at, and needless to say, would not be participating in my high school graduation ceremony. Everything checked out ok. Apparently, the drug I was given is also used for blood pressure issues and caused one of my heart valves to become dilated but not of immediate concern. I was sent home and told to try to take it easy so that my baby could have as much time as he needed to grow healthy and strong.

Four weeks later, at my 38 weeks check-in, the midwife I saw that day told me I was having contractions, so they were going to monitor me for a while in the office. She strapped on the monitors and left me to "relax" for about 30min. When she returned, she told me, "Congratulations! You're in labor and going to have your baby today!". This was strange to me because the contractions I had weren't that strong, and I was under the impression that labor was supposed to be the worst pain of my life. I went across the street to the hospital to have my baby anyway.

When I got to the area that I now know is called triage, the nurse did an internal exam and told me I was 3cm dilated and hooked me up to the monitors to confirm that I was in labor. She reported after a while that my contractions weren't really strong enough or in a good pattern and instructed me to walk around the hospital for 2 hours. I took this as more of an assignment to get things going better and decided to jog up and down the halls of the hospital. When I returned to triage, I was told it worked, and I would be admitted to have my baby. The contractions still were not painful at all.

At some point, I was hooked up to an IV and given Pitocin. I don't know any other details about it because I didn't question anything. I laid in the bed and listened to music for what seemed like forever. The day turned to night, and every single nurse that came in asked me if I was ready for my epidural. This made me increasingly angry because I have scoliosis and actually can't get an epidural. I used the breathing techniques I had learned to get through as the contractions got more and more painful from the Pitocin. After 21 hours, I finally felt the urge to push. Without any thought or hesitation, I flipped from lying down to on all fours and yelled out, "I have to poop!". The nurse told me to turn over on my back so she could fix all the wires and tubing, then call for the Dr. I just kept yelling out, "I have to poop!" at the top of my lungs. When the Dr. finally got there, she came in laughing and said she could hear me yelling as soon as she got off of the elevator. I was exhausted and hungry and just wanted my baby. My legs were put up in the stirrups, and I was then told to push as hard as I could. I pushed with all my might, and between pushes, I would fall asleep, snoring and all. I pushed him out fairly quickly, around 15-20 min., and felt so relieved. I don't even remember the birth of my placenta. She gave me two stitches and told me how good of a pusher I was. I held my son for a few minutes but honestly had very little interest in him at that moment. I had basic human needs that had been neglected the whole time I was in labor and just wanted to eat and drink. He would be taken to the NICU 24 hours later and then transferred to a children's hospital and diagnosed with Hirschsprung's Disease 3 days later.

I had no time to process his birth because I had to immediately switch to special needs mom and caregiver. We spent almost two months in the NICU, and through that experience, I learned a lot about dealing with the medical system and advocating.

When Sammy was two years old, we were involved in a terrible car accident, and he sustained a severe traumatic brain injury. Once again, I found myself by his side in the hospital for a few months. The year after the car accident, I was in school for nursing and heard about a training to become certified to teach breastfeeding classes from a dear friend. This would be a way for me to make money in the field I wanted to go into, labor and delivery, and gain experience with pregnant women. It was a retreat-style training held at The Farm in Tennessee. The farm is where the famous midwife Ina May Gaskin lived, worked, and trained midwives. I had seen the business of being born and was excited to meet the midwives there as well as learn everything I could from them. I went to The Farm with a wide-open mind and heart, ready to absorb; that's exactly what happened. I didn't learn much about teaching breastfeeding classes, but I learned so much about my true self and my calling to birth work. I had no idea there was such a thing as a doula and that I had unknowingly already been in that role supporting my close friend through her birth just a few months ago. I came back from that trip a different woman and never returned to nursing school. I signed up for what would be the first of several doula trainings and vowed to myself that I would take the next two years learning as much as I could about being a birth worker.

I traveled to several different states to learn from several different women and began supporting clients in the role of a doula. Throughout my trainings, I began to realize just how upside down, backward, and just wrong the birth I was supporting was. Many of the births I supported were in hospitals with OB's and what I now refer to as 'medwives,' and I realized how much they go entirely against human physiology and the physiology of birth. Never mind the complete disregard for the emotional state of the parents; oh wait, that's what I was there for. It became glaringly evident to me in the last 3 out of 8 years that I practiced as a doula that my role in a medical birth was to help the families be "ok" with and feel good about the trauma they were enduring. I was supposed to support all birth without judgment, which became more and more NOT ok with me. Through the years, I had supported a handful of hands-off home-births with midwives and a few unassisted births sprinkled in mostly because other doulas were, and still are, too afraid to attend.

After supporting undisturbed births vs. hospital and birth center births, I decided that when the time came for me to start having children again, I would freebirth(aka unassisted childbirth). I reflected on my first birth and realized how I was taken advantage of because I was young and naive. I saw that the weekend after my son was born on July 3rd, the fourth of July was that Friday, and it would've been a long weekend for my doctor. I was induced without understanding what was happening to me and coerced into it by all the medical staff involved. I was starved for almost 24hrs and forced to push on my back even though I instinctually wanted to be on all fours. I can't help but wonder how much different my mood would've been immediately after my birth if I wasn't induced, put on Pitocin, and starved for so long.

When I realized I was pregnant 10years later, I knew all of my free-birth dreams were about to become a reality. I knew my exact date of conception because my husband, Eli, and I were living in different states at the time due to him being in the military. I saw a midwife friend for some lab work and "proof of pregnancy," but I overall had what is known as a wild pregnancy, where you don't go in for any doctor or midwife appointments. I took my blood pressure a few times throughout and listened to my baby's heartbeat when I felt like I wanted to check-in in that way. I paid close attention to my diet and nutrition and tried to find time to take walks and be active. I took supplements when I felt like I needed to and really just tuned in to my body and what it was asking for. I saw a chiropractor for the third trimester, and that helped with a lot of the common aches that happen at the end of pregnancy. Because I had gone into preterm labor with Sammy and had him at 38 weeks, I just knew I wouldn't make it to my due date. Boy, was I wrong. My due date came and went. It caused me to reflect on my first pregnancy and birth once again and really consider the many factors that came into play causing the preterm labor and subsequent induction at 38 weeks. I had such a stress-free pregnancy this time around, and my body and my baby were just content. Knowing what I know now about the way your hormones affect your labor process, I understand why my first pregnancy and birth went the way they did. At almost 41 weeks pregnant, I was over at a friend's house and felt a tiny trickle. I knew it wasn't pee but just ignored it to see if it would happen again; it didn't. The next morning I went about my typical day and had some contractions throughout the day but nothing consistent or intense. That evening I had another little trickle, but this time I saw it and knew for sure it was my water. I went to sleep as usual, and nothing really happened through the night. The next morning, I woke up and had yet another trickle of amniotic fluid when I was saying goodbye to my husband as he left for work. I told him about the trickle, but I wasn't having consistent contractions, so no need for him to stay home from work. After breakfast, I decided to take Sammy out for a long walk around the neighborhood, just to see if that would get something going. I had a lot of contractions during the walk, but they slowed when we got back home. I continued through my day. During lunch, while on a call with my good friend, I started having more intense contractions. I just ignored them and cleaned up the kitchen when we were finished eating. Around 3, the contractions were not only more intense, but they were starting to come more frequently, so I knew this was labor starting. I debated whether I should call my husband to come home or not. He's in the military, and the process of getting a hold of him at work is not easy or straightforward. Because I knew he'd be off around 5, I decided just to lay down and see if that would help the contractions slow down a bit. I sent him a text letting him know he should come straight home after work and that I was going to lay down for a couple of hours until he got home. Laying down helped to space the contractions, and I'm pretty sure I took a nap. He called me when he got off, and I told him we would probably have the baby tonight, and I needed him to come set up the pool. I laid in bed until he arrived. Then I took one of the exercise balls in the shower and relaxed through my contractions in there. I predicted that when I got into a vertical position, the contractions would intensify, and they did. The playlist I made was on, and I was really able to zone out in the shower. About an hour later, he let me know the pool was ready and I could get in at any time. He went to get me some snacks and water, then got Sammy's dinner ready. I got in the pool, but it felt too hot, so I got out and got on all fours leaning and rocking on the other exercise ball. I got in and out of the pool a few times because I kept getting too hot and too cold. If I would've been in my "doula brain," I would've realized this was transition (the part of labor when your body dilates from 8cm-10cm, aka the most intense part when women often experience extreme temperature changes, shaking, vomiting, etc.). I eventually got back in the pool, and I just could not get comfortable or even into a rhythm with the contractions. I felt like I was flailing around the pool. My husband later told me it just looked like I was swimming around. In an attempt to figure out where in my labor I was, I checked my cervix.

I could definitely feel the sac of water, and it felt like there was still a good bit of cervix left, so I told Eli there was going to be at least a couple more hours left of labor. Two contractions later, my water fully broke, and I felt intense pressure. I was leaning over the pool and biting down on one of the handles to avoid pushing. I was panting instead. Eli had his arms under my armpits, kind of holding me up. I told him I needed to touch and got my arm free. I reached down between my legs and felt my baby's head. I freaked out for a moment and said, "Oh my God! It's too big. I can't fit!". And in the next moment, I reached down into the water and calmly pulled him up to my chest. He was so quiet. I sat back and rubbed him to try to arouse him. I knew he was ok, but I wanted the confirmation of hearing his little voice. We laid him on a towel on the edge of the pool and rubbed him with a dry towel, and told him we wanted to hear him. He let out the tiniest little squeal as if he was saying, leave me alone, please. So I scooped him up and placed him between my breasts as I sat back down into the water. He nursed a little, Eli brought me some pineapple juice, and we called our families to tell them he had arrived. About 30-40 minutes later, I was ready to get out and get cleaned up. As I started to stand up, I felt the urge to birth my placenta. I asked for a bowl to catch it in and pushed it out. I handed the baby to my husband and sat the bowl next to him so I could get out. This was the only part of the birth that he said made him nervous because he had never held a brand new baby and was afraid he might drop him. A friend of ours helped me get to the bathroom, get situated, and held the baby for a moment so Eli could start draining the pool. I got in bed, and we measured the baby and cut the cord. Eli finished cleaning everything, and I cut my placenta into pieces and put it in baggies to freeze for smoothies. My baby was born at 8:40 pm, and we were settled in bed by 11:30 pm. It was such a perfectly simple birth.

My own freebirth has inspired and motivated me to start speaking out about what I've known for a long time now. Birth is a normal, natural part of life that majority of the time, doesn't require any management and /or medical intervention. Six months later, I conceived again, and we are now having another wild pregnancy and preparing for another freebirth.

ALIA WRIGHT

Alia Wright is a wife and mother of three. She is passionate about all things pregnancy, birth, and mothering, as well as herbalism, home-making, and living a natural healthy lifestyle. Her experiences as both a special needs mom and a doula reframed the way she views the medical model of care and led her to freebirth (also known as unassisted birth), which has sent her on a path to supporting more women wanting to birth outside the system.

Website: aliawright.com
Email: alia.doesit@gmail.com
Facebook: https://www.facebook.com/alia.harper/
Instagram: https://www.instagram.com/alia_does/
Clubhouse: Alia Wright

12

FROM HOSPITAL BIRTHS TO HOME BIRTHS – AND BACK!

ASHLEY AUGUSTINE

THREE HOSPITAL BIRTHS, three home births, and planning a twin birth (not in that order)

As a mother of six, my births led me full circle from the conventional obstetrician and hospital delivery to choosing birth more tailored for me as an individual. As a childbirth educator and doula, I have been honored by attending many dozens of births, both in hospital and home settings. I learn something new about the birthing experience each and every time. I'm sharing the highlights of my personal journey that led me to find perfect peace with choosing home birth.

First born

As a pregnant college student working full-time, I had little time to research birth (if I did have an hour, it was stolen for a pregnancy-fatigue driven nap). As the eldest child in a family of eight, I had attended several peaceful natural births of my siblings, which fostered an innate trust in the birth process. That confidence lulled me into going with the flow with my prenatal care until my third trimester. I hoped to have an unmedicated birth. There were few thoughts less appealing than a large needle going through my spine; I was as certain that I didn't want an epidural as a first-time mom could be, with the inexperienced caveat of "unless I change my mind." There were no midwives or birth centers in my area, but a birth center near a hospital would have been appealing! My doctor made some slighting comments about unmedicated birth that undermined my confidence in the system and led me to seek out how to manage a natural birth in a hospital setting.

At 32 weeks pregnant, trusting the birth process, but looking down at my watermelon-sized belly, the thought of birthing an entire human was intimidating. I signed up for a Bradley Method Childbirth course to learn all I could. It is normally a twelve-week series, but since I didn't have that much time, the passionate instructor, Mary Ellen, condensed it down into six for us. My husband Brady was initially skeptical. He was marginally supportive of my desire for a natural birth, but admittedly held a professed faith in "all modern medicine has to offer." However, by our second class, rich with birth information and comfort measures, his perception shifted and he even recommended the course to coworkers. Through the course, we learned about the labor process, ways to navigate the hospital environment, and lowering intervention risks. I was determined not to induce labor or go to the hospital too early because both seemed to lead to higher cesarean rates. We finished our childbirth crash course, and passed my due date. At 41 weeks and 3 days I felt antsy, walked several miles, ate spicy food, and went on a windy boat ride. That seemed to do the trick, and light contractions started coming about every 10-14 minutes.

Determined to get labor going in earnest, I walked for miles at 3 a.m. while my husband slept (I do *not* recommend walking in the middle of the night, for future reference). That made for a long night, and we hung out at home the entire next day, a Sunday. Contractions stayed right around 10 minutes apart, and were very manageable. I hoped that the consistent contractions were making progress, but it all seemed mild. The pace picked up that evening, and around 5 a.m. Monday, with strong contractions about 5 minutes apart, we headed to the hospital. At arrival, I was 5 centimeters dilated. Disappointed that after more than a day of contractions that I was barely halfway, I told myself it could change quickly. However, it did not. I was assigned an unsupportive nurse who kept pushing that I sign the epidural paperwork, "because EVERYONE wants it, Honey, you *will* want it," and who was also insistent on very frequent fetal monitoring. Being in the bed for the monitors to get a proper read caused much more pain and slowed my contractions. Though his heartrate was perfect, the nurse was adamant about keeping the rigid schedule. The incessant interruptions, bright lights, machines beeping, hall noises, and uncomfortable monitors were a hinderance to normal labor; the change in my contraction pattern was perfect evidence of how disruptive the environment was. When I could get out of the bed and move, my labor pattern would pick back up. My contractions were very manageable with the comfort measures we had learned, especially back counterpressure, relaxation, and massage. My mother came, and Mary Ellen joined us as doula, and their encouragement and positive presence transfigured the atmosphere.

It never occurred to me that people would show up to a birth without invitation. We did not anticipate visitors, so we had not been proactive about protecting our birth space. Throughout the day, relatives dropped into our hospital room unannounced, and others sent well wishes from the waiting room. Every time labor was disturbed by a visitor popping in or a nurse wanting to monitor, contractions slowed down, and the day dragged on. Three times I entered transition, which was exciting but intense work with powerful back-to-back contractions, but then labor would be disrupted by someone, and things would slack back off before gradually resuming intensity. That evening, my doctor checked me and announced, "You are 8 centimeters, your waterbag is bulging, and if I break it, you'll be pushing within thirty minutes." I consented, and he was right. I pushed hard, trying multiple positions. Pushing felt productive and was a welcome change! Suddenly the room was packed with new faces, and nurses around my bed were shouting "PUSH! PUSH!" with each contraction. I didn't understand why there was such urgency in their voices, and thought that something must be wrong with my baby. I felt distressed and pushed with all I had. The feeling of overwhelming release as he was born was unforgettable, and he was handed to me, wide-eyed, slippery, and warm. Filled with wonder, we felt the cord pulse and waited to clamp it. His chubby neck rolls reminded me of a shar-pei puppy. He was very healthy, and a whopping 9 lb., 9 oz. which probably played a part in the longer labor. There had been no cause for concern. The nurses' tone was just their usual push coaching. He latched and nursed right away, and was amazingly alert. I went headfirst into the joy of babymoon. The next day as we were checking out to go home, my OB commented, "as big as he was, and as hard as you had to push to get him out, if you had gotten an epidural you would have had a cesarean." I was incredibly thankful for having taken the childbirth course, having a supportive doula, and having tools and knowledge to navigate a pregnancy going past my due date and longer labor. My natural birth was empowering and inspirational; I was always excited to share about birth with friends. *Birth stats: 41 weeks, 5 days. Hospital birth. Total labor: 46 hours. Active labor: 22 hours. Baby boy, 9 lb., 9 oz. Time at the hospital before birth: 15 hours.*

Second time

Nine months later, prompted by a couple of days of nausea, I learned that I was expecting. It was a surprise, my cycle had not returned, but I knew that breastfeeding was unreliable for keeping fertility at bay. I decided to remain with the same OB-Gyn at the rural hospital, mostly out of convenience as I had a tolerable-enough experience with my first birth. We re-enrolled in childbirth classes with Mary

Ellen for the full experience and more practice in preparation. Because in my first birth after admitting labor felt more disturbed than fluid, and progress slowed, my biggest concern was going to the hospital too soon. My plan was to labor undisturbed at home as long as possible, ideally to admit at transition, push the baby out, and go home as soon as humanely possible, to minimize the interruptions in both labor and postpartum. I prayed for a 'manageable, shorter labor' because physically, the hardest part had been exhaustion. I hoped that if everything went more smoothly, as a second birth often does, that I would have a fifteen-hour labor. That idea seemed great and so doable, with less time for disturbances. My pregnancy went well, and the only hiccup was that I tested group beta-strep positive, which dictates that antibiotics are to be administered four hours before birth. I didn't want to go in that early. My doctor was adamant that any deviation would be malpractice and there was no other option. I didn't feel I would be able to accurately guess when four hours before delivery would be and hated the idea of unnecessary antibiotics, so I sought a second opinion. I consulted a maternal-fetal specialist OB-Gyn, known to be conservative and natural birth friendly. He said antibiotics were standard, however, without risk factors such as prematurity or long rupture of membranes, that it was unlikely for a baby to acquire a strep infection. He went on to say that statistically, the risk of a hospital-acquired infection was actually higher than the GBS risk and that the GBS test wasn't even administered in Europe! He surprised me by saying, "If you are concerned about infection and want a natural birth, why don't you give birth at home with a midwife?"

"Oh, I would love to do that!" I exclaimed, "but there are no midwives in my area." He smiled mischievously, and knowing my mother, said, "Your mother had eight children, she's practically qualified to assist at home, but if you want to transfer to me, I will deliver in hospital if you decline antibiotics." I went home amazed at his trusting and open attitude toward the birth process and his honesty with the actual statistical risk that my OB seemed to be magnifying. After researching and discussing with my husband, who was vehemently opposed to switching doctors and traveling an hour in labor, I went against my intuition and stayed at the rural practice. I made peace with the fact that I would go in earlier and receive antibiotics.

Three days before my due date, in a flurry of energy, I deep-cleaned my entire house and cooked a feast for dinner. A friend commented, "it sounds like you are nesting. You are probably going to have your baby soon!" to which I laughed, "Oh no, this baby is comfortable, and no signs of labor. I'll probably be pregnant for another two weeks!" I woke around 11:30 pm that night with a throbbing backache. I quietly got out of bed and immersed myself in warm water in our antique porcelain tub. Shortly after midnight, I realized that the pain seemed to ebb and flow about every five minutes, timed almost like a contraction; I wondered if it could possibly be the start of back labor. With my first, I felt pulling sensations in the front, like a menstrual cramp, but this was totally different. Slightly past midnight, after increasingly intense cramps at very consistent intervals, I woke my husband to tell him that labor *might* be starting. By one a.m., it was unmistakable, with powerful contractions coming every four or five minutes. My mother arrived to pick up our sleeping toddler. She took one look at me, deeply in labor, and said, "Don't wait too long to go!" Adamant that I would *not* be interrupted and strapped to monitors for a full day of labor, I said, "I'm not going too early because that made me so miserable last time!" "Just don't wait too long," she insisted. In my mind, *if I was lucky*, I was going to have that 15-hour labor (or longer), so I was preparing to work all day. The strength of the contractions took me aback; they were intense, fast, and overwhelming. I didn't realize it, but the contractions had started coming about three minutes apart. I told Brady, "This hurts worse than it *ever* did last time!" Barely an hour into labor, he didn't understand and said, "you have had a bad attitude this whole pregnancy," and for that remark I kicked him with my foot from where I was side-lying in the bed. The contractions were double peaking and all-consuming. I felt that none of my relaxation techniques that helped last time were working as well. My muscles twisting inside felt like a mop being wrung out, with hurricane-force intensity. I wondered how on earth I could maintain this pace for twelve or fifteen more hours. It was so overwhelming that it seemed impossible. "I mean it," I said. "*When* we get to the hospital, I want to get the meds."

There was *no* moment in my first labor where I wanted an epidural; I had felt tired and that it was hard work, but I was able to manage the discomfort with relaxation and comfort measures. This was different, so wild and intense. There was no management; it was like riding a ship tossed in a storm. His eyes were large at my statement, having seen me labor for two days and never say anything remotely like that. "Ok, let's go to the hospital then," he said, to which I responded, "There is *no way* it is time to go! I'm not going for them to disturb my labor and make it hurt more all day long! But, when we *do* go, I want all the meds." I had two more earth-shattering contractions that rocked my whole being and added: "*and* I don't ever want to do this again. I don't want any more kids". At that, Brady became worried because he knew that a large family was something very dear to me, and for me to say that, I must feel extremely serious. "If you feel that strongly, I think we need to go." Hearing his stern tone, my brain came out of its labor-focus and processed that he was probably right; Mary Ellen had emphasized that deep seriousness is a sign you may be approaching transition or birth. I stood up to prepare to leave for the hospital and felt my baby shift lower and pressure dramatically increase. "Okay. I'm going to the bathroom first, and then we'll go."

Waddling to the toilet, I sat and realized then that I didn't need the bathroom at all. I reached down and could feel the top of my baby's head crowning just inside—membranes still intact. I shouted, "The baby's coming RIGHT NOW!" Brady ran in the door, saw my eyes wide with fright, and sputtered,

"Well, we have to go then!"

"No, there is no time. The head is *right there*."

I stepped off the toilet and into the tub (still filled with warm water from my soak just an hour before), and at the next powerful contraction, without pushing, baby's forehead came out, facing my left thigh, slightly oddly positioned. Brady called 911 using speaker phone, and the dialogue was comical, with them questioning if his wife was *actually* having a baby until he said, "I can see the baby's eyebrows." After ineptly flipping pages in a manual, they told him to get me out of the tub and into a bed because that's what their procedure called for. "Hang up with them and call my mom!" I exclaimed, knowing she'd offer more help, but there was no time for that as the next contraction began. He set the phone down, and with the next contraction, my baby slipped out through the water and into my arms. He let out a healthy cry and breathed well, but his face was oddly purple compared to his quickly-pink body. It made me afraid that he had gone without oxygen in the birth canal. I put him to the breast to nurse, and he responded and latched readily, which helped the placenta come shortly after. It was before 2 a.m., so he was in my arms less than two hours from the first recognizable contractions. Brady told the 911 operator not to send an ambulance and called my mother. She helped me clean up, and we drove to the hospital to have the baby examined (the color of his face still concerned me, though he seemed perfect otherwise). I hurried through the double doors, my baby cradled in my arms, walking through long corridors of the hospital to get to labor and delivery; Brady was tugging my shirt back saying, "slow down, you just had a baby." I felt great, like I had run a sprint instead of having given birth. Coming up to the shoulder-high nurse counter and briskly announcing my name, they asked, "are you in labor?" to which I lifted my newborn up over the counter for them to see and said, "we actually just had him really fast at home and need to have him checked out." After a collective gasp, the younger nurse asked, "do we put them in labor and delivery or a postpartum room?" My baby was perfectly healthy, but they required a two-day stay for him to receive antibiotic injections for my beta-strep status and because he "was born in a non-sterile environment," which was an unpleasant experience (and unnecessary, with research in retrospect). According to my OB, the purple tone of his face was simply bruising from his cruising through the birth canal in a sideways position so fast, and it quickly subsided. *Birth stats: 39 weeks, 4 days. Unplanned, unassisted home birth. Water break: moment of crowning. Total labor: about 2 hours. Active labor: about 1.5 hours. Baby weight: 8 lb. 8 oz. Baby boy.*

Third Time's a Charm

One might think after an (accidental) home birth experience that I would have been immediately sold on the idea, but my kneejerk take-away from it was that I would never want to have an unassisted birth. Those few moments when his face was purple, and no one else was in charge, or could offer support or assurance that he was healthy, were frightening. It didn't help that many people assumed that we had planned an unassisted birth, and openly judged that choice, so I felt like I was constantly retelling my story with the caveat "I just never expected to have a baby in less than 2 hours after having a 46-hour labor!". Three years after that, I was expecting my third son, and I switched to the MFM OB-Gyn who had consulted so favorably about natural birth. My pregnancy was great, my OB supported and respected parental decisions and informed consent. He was a breath of fresh air, and the larger hospital staff working with him seemed to follow his supportive tone.

Around 39 weeks, we were hosting friends for supper when spilled pepper caused a sneezing fit and my water broke. We sent our two children home with friends to spend the night, and within an hour I was contracting in earnest. We left for the hospital without delay, anxious of the commute after my precipitous birth, and called my doctor, who met us there. The monitoring was intermittent and not bothersome; the nurses left us to ourselves for the most part. I felt very supported as I found my rhythm, having stronger contractions than with my first but without the wild storm intensity of my second birth. When I requested a birth ball to lean on, the nurse dribbled it down the entire hospital hallway to bring to me, (YUCK) so then I didn't want my skin touching it, but that was my *only* complaint. The staff supported my birth plan and was respectful. After four hours of steadily increasing but manageable contractions and a lot of back counterpressure from my husband, my son was born! During pushing, the doctor and nurses were quiet and let me follow my own pattern uninterrupted. He was beautiful, perfect, and nursed wonderfully.

Everything about the birth was great, as smooth as I've ever thought a hospital birth could be, but our good experience stopped there. Our regular pediatrician didn't round at that hospital, so the on-call pediatrician provided oversight. For reasons still unknown to us, instead of releasing us on the second day after birth, the pediatrician was adamant that we stay an *additional* two more days for monitoring. When asked for a reason, he said we needed to take the baby's temperature a couple of times a day. I told him I could take his temperature at home every two hours if needed and asked what the concern was as his bloodwork had come back clear—but he gave us no answer. Upon discussing this with the nurses, they agreed there was no medical reason for us to stay. One nurse even remarked, "you need to take that baby home!" So we did, signing a form for withdrawing against medical advice. This necessitated speaking to a child welfare representative on the way out, who thankfully heard the nurse's perspective, and responded, "this seems to make sense. I'm not sure why I was even called." Though she was supportive, having to speak to child welfare to go home was exceptionally stressful. Once home, postpartum was easy and joyful with a happy baby that fit right in to our family. *Birth Stats: 39-week hospital birth. Water break: 6 hours, 5 hours active labor. Time at the hospital: 4 hours. Baby weight 8 lb. 14 oz. Baby boy.*

Something a little different

Pregnant with my fourth, I seriously considered birthing in a newly opened birth center with a midwife. We toured, interviewed the midwife, and felt very drawn to it, but the downsides were that it was over an hour away, and financially it would be a major stretch. My three boys were older (nine, seven, and four), and I pragmatically told myself that "your hospital births weren't *so* bad, you could take the thousands extra the birth center would cost and take an unforgettable family vacation with the boys before baby, or it could be spent on one day." After some soul-searching, we decided to take a two-week family road trip to Rocky Mountain and Yellowstone National Parks, and give birth again in the hospital, covered-by-insurance. It was an amazing adventure. Sadly, my wonderful MFM OB had retired to a teaching position since my third was born, so I chose a new doctor on a friend's recommendation.

This OB was decidedly more paternalistic, and I missed the feeling of being respected as an active participant in my care. When I requested research on the newly recommended flu vaccine, given in pregnancy for the first time that year, his words to me were, "if you were my wife, I'd stick you with it in your sleep," to which I replied, "It's a good thing I'm not your wife!" His condescending attitude permeated interactions, but I didn't know of any better in-hospital option. In my late third trimester, I had a severe pain develop near the top of my uterus, and I brought it up at several appointments. The OB dismissed it as normal pregnancy discomfort, but it was unlike anything I ever felt before. I described it to him as "It feels like a wound or bruise, and when baby moves, it is like they are plucking the wound, or hitting an injured organ." To impress how seriously I felt, I continued—even though I knew it was a bit ridiculous sounding, "It isn't possible for the baby to kick a hole in the placenta, is it? Because this feels like a wound being poked when she moves?" He laughed at me and said that wasn't a concern.

Three weeks prior to my due date, I woke up to a pop as my water broke on New Year's Day, and as it gushed, it seemed to be more blood than water. My husband was at work, so my father rushed me to the hospital, worried for my child's life and praying the entire time. My baby looked perfect on the monitor, and by then the amniotic leak was stopped by her head, so I continued to labor naturally. I did have constant monitoring due to reporting bleeding, but her heart never missed a beat. Despite the circumstances, I was able to tune the distractions out. Closing my eyes, focusing on being relaxed, and going into a deep introspective mindset, it was my most peaceful labor yet. With it being a holiday, my OB was not working, and the OB on call was friendly and respectful. I sat quietly cross-legged on the bed and rode out the waves of contractions with focused deep relaxation, feeling mild discomfort but no difficult pains. My husband met us as soon as he could, and 20 minutes later, I delivered her in one pushing contraction. As she was born, all the deep red fluid contained behind her burst out as well. Upon inspecting the placenta, the OB showed me a small half-moon tear that I had been internally bleeding from. That was the pain I had been feeling for weeks, with no other outward sign, and could have ended badly for one or both of us had it continued. He said it had been present for over a month and that it was as incredibly rare as a lightning strike. He had only seen one such tear before in his career. It was terrifying to know that the symptoms I had elaborated on had been ignored when there was a life-threatening issue lurking.

Born so abruptly (just one push), she had aspirated amniotic fluid into her lungs and had some breathing difficulties, so she was sent to the NICU for breathing assistance and oxygen. I was assured she'd be brought right back, but after 3 hours, I insisted on going to see her, my first baby girl. They had already given her formula and put her on the standard precautionary antibiotics that all NICU babies receive. Because of the blood in the amniotic fluid, they didn't know how long it would take to resolve from her lungs, and told me to prepare for a two-week stay. It felt incredibly empty and lonely to be postpartum and not holding or nursing my baby! Having never responded well to a breast pump, collecting colostrum was difficult, and I spent every moment that I was allowed at her bedside in the NICU; there were times parents were banned. She surpassed all breathing expectations, and by the third day was able to come completely off of oxygen, but they told me that because they'd given her formula, it would shock her system to go straight to my milk, and she had to stay two more days to slowly wean from the formula to my milk as it came in.

Sitting at her isolette, surrounded by other tiny babies also receiving care, my time in the NICU opened my eyes to conventional medical practices that were off-putting and scary. While I was thankful for the care and oxygen she received, it was incredibly frustrating to feel like an accessory to her life. Decisions were made without consulting or notifying me. I would find out later that everything on my birth plan was disregarded for protocol—declining eye ointment, for example, which has nothing to do with breathing difficulties. It was exceptionally frustrating that two final days were spent not needing medical assistance but simply to wean her off of formula I'd never consented to, instead of me being able to breastfeed. Meeting feeding requirements seemed an inadequate reason to be locked in a room with limited visiting hours and a baby ankle bracelet, much less a multi-thousand-dollar daily price tag. We were incredibly thankful to finally take her home on the sixth day, but it was a very stressful postpartum time. I second-guessed every decision I made as a parent, an odd feeling after confidently parenting three others. Looking back, I pondered how much the NICU experience played into my postpartum anxiety, and since I've seen much research correlating the two. *Birth stats: 37 weeks. Hospital birth. Water break: 4.5 hours. Active labor: 3 hours. Baby weight 7 lb. 4 oz. Baby Girl.*

Coming Home

Two years later, I was pregnant with our fifth baby. I felt full of
apprehension as I went to an initial appointment with my former OB.
He reassured me (after my question and flipping pages to read the on-
call doctor's notes) that the placenta tear was a fluke and I was at no
increased risk of that happening again. I realized that I had no peace
going back under his care. I needed to feel respected, yearned for
more individualized attention, and I wanted to know exactly who
would be making decisions at my bedside. I wanted someone who
knew me and would take my concerns and symptoms seriously.
Coming from a bad experience with my third baby with a strange
pediatrician, and following that with a pregnancy with dismissed
complication and a postpartum where almost every decision was
taken out of my hands, I never wanted to be in that situation again. I
wanted to be with carefully selected care providers, where I wasn't
just a rushed slot on the schedule, and in whom I could trust. After
searching, I found a well-qualified home birth midwife, Anne
Lastrapes, who had decades of experience both as a nurse and
Midwife, who would deliver in my rural area. I wasted no time inter-
viewing her (with pages of questions) and felt that every piece fell
into place for what I was looking for in a care team that was both
attentive and conscientious. I switched doctors to a Midwife-
supportive OB for the required prenatal appointments and decided
to go with a home birth early in my pregnancy.

Each prenatal appointment was a fresh breeze; Anne, and her
student midwife, Michel, were amazing. Visits were not rushed, and
they took time to talk about the whole picture of health: diet, exercise,
my life outside of just being a pregnant person, and attended to every
pregnancy detail. They would palpate and estimate the baby's position, check heart rate and measurements, and do other standard
testing each time. After just a few meetings, going to a visit felt like a
lunch date with close friends and became something I treasured.

They attended to every detail, and answered questions completely and thoroughly. I knew that they were fully capable of handling birth and I was reassured that they would not hold back if they felt a transfer of care was medically needed.

My labor started at 39 weeks with a water break as it had for my two previous babies. After a couple of hours, contractions got into a regular pattern, and with my fast birth history, Anne and Michel came to my home. I was surprised with how much equipment they brought, even an oxygen tank! My room looked like a birthing suite once the sterile area was all set and ready. I labored in peace in my bedroom with my husband providing comfort measures. The birth team checked on me as needed, but for the most part, left my husband and I together undisturbed. My dear friend Sarah attended as doula/photographer and brought cool cloths, warm tea, and saw to other things as needed. Her presence was a joy and a comfort because while my husband was being my physical support-rubbing my back, or letting me sway and rest my head on his chest—she was attending to the little details, such as refreshment or adjusting the light. After about five hours of utterly peaceful active labor, I quietly pushed my fifth son into the world, on hands-and-knees, in the comfort of my own bed. He went right into Michel's arms, and then I was able to carefully flip around and take him into mine. He was perfect, cried enough to breathe well, and was calm and alert overall.

I was laughing with happiness and overjoyed at the whole process. It felt calming, comforting, and my family felt whole. Shortly after, my older children piled in to meet their new brother, and a few hours after that other close family members dropped by. It was so relaxed and truly joyful. I *loved* birthing at home, but postpartum at home was *even better*. I had all my own comforts, clothing, and could adjust things exactly the way I wanted them. I was completely overcome with a sense of gratitude for having had such a beautiful, supported and peaceful experience. There were no unwelcome intrusions or machines beeping, no strangers introducing themselves around the clock to care for us. The midwives monitored us for several hours, weighed and monitored baby, cleaned and left my room pristine, gave guidelines for newborn care, and told me they would be back the next morning for our first well check. We knew we could reach them in a moment with any question. It was a brilliant day, and I will always reflect fondly on it. *Birth Stats: 39-week Home birth with midwives. Water break: 10 hours. Active labor: about 4-5 hours. Baby weight 8 lb. 2 oz. Baby Boy.*

Another holiday surprise

It was quite natural that when I became pregnant again five years later that I didn't have the slightest hesitation to choose home birth again. Anne had retired, but Michel was fully certified and would travel to my home for the birth of our sixth baby. I was thrilled to be utilizing midwifery care and planning a homebirth again, knowing I was in phenomenal hands that I already had a great relationship with. I felt great and stayed active, gaining less than my other pregnancies, so I was anticipating my smallest baby. The day after my due date, at 1 pm, my water broke while I was scrubbing baseboards (apparently nesting is real). My husband was on a helicopter in the middle of the Gulf of Mexico, and his company had to radio him in. He was five hours from home. Contractions came on slowly and were mild and sporadic until about 5 pm. Shortly before he got home, things picked up, and Michel and her assistant SarahBeth came over. Wanting to share the beauty of a peaceful home birth experience, I invited my sister and sisters-in-law over and kept my eight-year-old daughter present. I didn't seem to labor as intently while chatting and enjoying their company, so Michel suggested that I retreat to my bedroom for a more secluded environment. The contraction intensity picked up immediately, and I progressed to completely dilated by about 10 pm, but the baby was still high, and I didn't feel the urge to push. It was October 30[th,] and I was hoping to have my baby before midnight. I didn't want him to share his birthday with Halloween, but at 11:30pm, when I finally began pushing, I realized it wasn't going to go quickly. He slowly worked his way down, and with encouragement, I pushed with all that I had to get him out, again on my hands and knees. I remember the sensation of stretching to what felt like maximum amount, and then *more*, my most strenuous pushing phase yet to date. When his head finally came out, I expected his body to slip out as the others, but it required more forceful pushing, as he was born incredibly slowly and took a little while to cry. Michel exclaimed, "Well, that's why it took time, that's a big baby!" He had chub rolls from his chin down to his ankles, and I said "That's a ten-pound baby!" My daughter unwrapped his towel and proudly announced, "It's a boy!" After admiring and cuddling him for a bit, he weighed in at 10 lbs, 8 oz, born at 12:51 on October 31st. He was my largest by a solid pound and my second-longest labor of all.

Amazingly, I did not need any sutures or repair—apparently fat squishes well, and I credited the slow presentation. As a doula, I've seen many slower/bigger baby births in hospitals, and they were never so peacefully managed, always pushed or forced. If someone had been pulling on him, I have no doubt it would have caused damage instead of him being able to ease his way down and out without harm. Michel and Sarabeth brought an infectious feeling of joy with their attitude and demeanor, and were so supportive throughout. The longer and more strenuous pushing phase was harder than my previous births, but I was so happy and thankful to have been at home with such competent care providers. *Birth stats: 40 weeks, 1 day. Home birth with midwives. Water break: 12 hours. Active labor: about 6 hours. Baby weight: 10 lb. 8 oz. Baby Boy.*

Double Encore

After my two amazing home births and attending many dozens of births as a doula both in hospitals and at homes, witnessing protocols that are not structured for individualized care happening as routine in hospitals, I could never imagine intentionally planning another hospital birth for myself. When my sixth child was two years old, I got another positive pregnancy test and immediately called Michel to reserve space on her calendar. However, during my initial exam ultrasound, my OB paused and then said, "Here is the heartbeat... and here is the OTHER heartbeat!" As luck would have it, we are expecting identical twins, and here in Louisiana, midwives cannot legally assist out-of-hospital twin births. I'll be going back to a hospital to welcome our seventh and eighth babies. My OB oversaw my prenatal appointments for my last home birth, has worked with midwives, is natural birth supportive and very respectful, and has a low cesarean rate. I am in good hands. I'm hoping to be able to have a doula and incorporate as much peace as possible into this hospital birth. My grandfather *and* great-grandfather were both identical twins, with a close and treasured relationship. This created a fondness for twins throughout our entire family, so that surprise was received with tremendous joy. With all the medical changes that come with twins, such as birthing in the operating room instead of a labor suite, this birth will likely be very different. I'm disappointed to let go of so much that I loved about home birth: autonomy, freedom, and a more individualized standard of care. Regardless of how the birth will play out, I'm thrilled for the opportunity to meet these two little blessings!

Epilogue

It is worth mentioning that I have had three miscarriages over the years; two were early, and one was in the second trimester. All were loved, and all are missed. My late miscarriage was midwife-supported at home, and a peaceful and empowering way to bring a lost baby earthside. I had concurrent care with my midwife-supportive OB. In my experience, there has been no medical service to parallel the level of midwifery care, and midwife-supportive, evidence-based OBs provide the best standard of care in their field.

After my first midwife-supported home birth, I was so moved with the perfection and peace of the experience, that I wanted to help others attain their best birth. I became certified as a childbirth educator and doula, and have since been honored to be a part of mothers' journeys and attend many births. Every birth is unique, and there is always something to learn. The following are tidbits of wisdom that each of my six births imparted upon me:

1) A mother's body is amazingly powerful, designed to bring a child into this world and fully nurture it! Interventions and distractions take away from labor, and it is important to conserve energy and protect your birth space.

2) Pay attention to the signs of labor, and don't let preconceived notions or numbers in your head cast projections on how the birth process will be.

3) Be selective with all healthcare providers that will work with you and your baby. The importance of a trustworthy care provider is paramount.

4) Birth *can* be peaceful and even not painful, but also that it is crucial to listen to your body and intuition when something is not right.

5) With the right team and preparation, birth can be *absolutely magical*.

6) Don't place expectations on birth! It will always surprise you. You can have the best laid plans, but be ready to go with the flow.

Hopefully my birth stories will offer insight and perspective for both hospital and home birth experiences. As a doula, I strongly encourage you to research your options, knowing that it is *your* body, and *your* birth story, so please choose what is best for *you*. If you seek out the resources and providers who will help you achieve your goals, you will realize your best birth. Birth is kind of like a box of chocolates-you never really know what you are going to get!

Resources:
Michel Martien, CPM, LM https://www.acadianamidwifery.com
Sarahbeth Boyd, CPM, LM https://www.acadianamidwifery.com
The Bradley Method of Natural Childbirth www.BradleyBirth.com

ASHLEY AUGUSTINE

Ashley Augustine is a mother of six (soon to be eight) children in southwest Louisiana. Having found birth to be a transformational passage into parenthood, she is passionate about sharing information and helping mothers navigate their options to plan for their best birth. She is a certified birth doula, and teaches childbirth education classes. She loves photography and capturing beautiful moments, especially at births. When not involved in pregnancy and birth work, she is schooling her children at home and at large, enjoying travel whenever the opportunity permits.

Website: www.SWLABirthServices.com
Email: SWLABirth@gmail.com
Facebook: https://www.facebook.com/SWLABirthServices

13

FINDING YOUR SECRET INGREDIENTS

THE STORY OF A HOME BIRTH AFTER TWO EMPOWERING HOSPITALS BIRTHS.

BETHANY A. LECLERC CD(DONA), CLC, APPAC

THERE IS SOMETIMES an unspoken pressure on a doula. The pressure to have the secret ingredients to make a family's birth everything they want it to be. Doulas work tirelessly through research, education, and experience to find those specific ingredients for that very recipe. Spinning Babies, rebozo, mindful birthing, hypnosis, evidenced based birth, these are all part of this magic potion, but there is a catch. The most important ingredients for a good birth are often ideas and expectations a doula has no control over. Only a birth giver as an individual, sometimes with help from a doula, can decipher what they are and what their priority in their birth will be. They are different for everyone, and there isn't one recipe better than another because we don't all have the same elements to work with. Also, our ideas, visions, and expectations change based on our individual circumstances, backgrounds, the information we receive, and what we believe to be true. My own experiences, along with the incredible families I have worked with as a doula, helped me to find mine. Hopefully, my stories, and others in this book, will help birthing families to find and recognize theirs. My decision to have a home birth was less a result of hospital trauma with myself or those I may have witnessed, and more because the culmination of my own past births, along with those I have supported, helped me to shape what ingredients were essential for me.

Birth #1

Labor and birth are such a hush-hush subject in our everyday societal life. Even as someone who works in the birth world, it is rare I hear people talking about their birth experience and, sadly, rarer to hear someone talk about their birth in a positive light. Ninety percent of birthing people are whisked off to a hospital, and only providers and nurses see labor and birth unfold and the baby born into the world. Many women during their first pregnancy are coming into their experience with absolutely no knowledge or background on birth and with maybe nine months to get it all in. This was me too. I was a clean slate for the birth of my first born. I held a healthy perception of birth developed from witnessing my sister give birth when I was 12. My mother had allowed me to attend, thinking it might be a wonderful experience but also a form of birth control. It did not have the exact effect she was looking for. My sister was the definition of happiness throughout the entire experience. If there was fear or unfathomable pain happening in the room, it was unbeknownst to me. When I became pregnant with my first child, I knew I wanted to go the unmedicated route, largely because of what I had witnessed with my sister. I thought, I can do that. Labor and birth were new to me, however, so I read books I was told to read at the time by close friends. Some of the books were about birth in general, and some were focused on positive birth stories. The books ended up being even more helpful than the four-week, three hour "natural" birth education course my husband and I took. I was eager to find tools in this class to manage labor but apparently, going natural meant breathing slowly with the sound of waves in a dark room with your partner behind you.

My actual birth showed me I was going to need a few more tools for the actual management of labor. I'm sure my husband gained some insight on birth, though, for which I was grateful. Reading birth stories, however, helped me to shape my expectations and ideas around labor and birth. I found reading about how other women labored and what worked for them made my birth experience easier to imagine. Nowadays, a podcast like The Birth Hour or the Evidenced Based Birth Podcast have an even greater impact. These podcasts interview birth givers and use their birth stories and fact-based information to educate others. I did receive the "you're crazy for wanting to do this unmedicated" comment often, but for some reason, it never phased me. It also helped my husband gave unwavering support to however I wanted to birth.

With the advice of a dear friend who had had the type of birth experience I admired, I left my OB practice and found a midwife at another local hospital. At first, I was nervous, but I remember feeling a deep relief when I saw the very books I had been reading on her bookshelf. I thought, "ok, I really think I can have the birth I want, supported by someone who maybe gets me." Today, nine years later, watching others choose or simply deal with their providers, despite how they feel, I see the positive impact choosing her had on my experience. It is never too late to find a provider you feel great about. Going with the flow in this choice won't benefit you as the birth giver or anyone who gives birth in the future. If we aren't thoughtful as birth givers about who provides our care, changes and updates in evidenced-based practices won't happen.

The day my labor started; I was 40 weeks plus 1 day. I had gone into the practice for a check-in. One of the midwives gave me a cervical check and offered a membrane sweep. She also recommended I begin taking evening primrose oil capsules vaginally. As a doula, if my client asked, I would give the evidence as to why some of those management techniques have risks, but, again, I was a clean slate. I was walking into the pharmacy to buy the evening primrose oil that very evening when I felt my first contraction. I clearly remember it rippling through me as I stood in the cold parking lot of the pharmacy. I was so excited. After purchasing the capsules, I went home and waited. They kept coming, though manageable and far apart. I remember being shocked when I called the hospital at 4am, and no one answered the phone. When I finally did find someone in labor and delivery to talk with, they told me to go back to sleep. I obliged, a sign I was clearly still in early labor. I just wanted someone to talk to who knew what was happening, to tell me everything was normal, ok. I proceeded through the next day, watching the series Spartacus, a rather violent choice in retrospect, and being lazy on the couch. When things picked up at 4pm the next day, and sensations were about every 5 minutes, we decided to go into the hospital.

The drive to the hospital sticks with me. I cranked the volume on the radio and proceeded to panic a bit, exacerbating the sensations, which seemed to intensify while we drove. On arrival to the hospital, I was checked and was at 3cm. I was disappointed—still quite a long way to go. The midwife I knew and adored was there with another newer midwife who she assigned to me. She stated to her, "I would be a textbook birth." I was ok with this. I was told I could go home or see what happened if I stayed. I chose to stay, especially with the drive there fresh in my mind. Around 10pm, the midwife told me I was 6cm, and I felt defeated. She mentioned if she broke my waters[1] I would likely progress more quickly. No mention of the fact my extreme back labor may mean the baby was in a less than ideal position. To me, "progress more quickly" was exactly what I wanted to hear. Quickly after my waters broke, the back labor, which already had my husband giving me consistent double hip squeezes on the ball, tripled in intensity. I felt as if my back would snap in half. I could not bear the thought of going through the sensations without his pressure on my lower back. Thankfully, I did progress, and by 1am I was ready to push. I ended up being on the bed solely so the midwife at the time could check to see if I was ready to push. She confirmed and I never moved. There was absolutely mention of trying other positions, but I had no interest. There were also some votes on what time each person in the room thought our baby would arrive, 2am, 3am, 4am. None of them wound up winning.

At one point I did try tug-of-war with the sheet tied to the bar attached to the bed. This position seemed to give me some umph. The newer midwife who was supposed to be attending, "a textbook birth," did eventually bring in the midwife I knew and adored. My midwife provided verbal support along with the nurse and my husband on either side of me. With their encouragement and sheer will, I thought, "I could do this." Four hours of pushing, and there was some talk of having one of the OBs come in to use a vacuum. I did not like the sound of that. I gave it my all from that point forward. We had not found out the gender, and to be honest, when my little boy, Mateo Axel, was born at 5:15am, sunny side up, I didn't think to even question it. With a big cone head and a small and somewhat bloody bruise on his head, he couldn't have been more alert. We looked right at each other, and my heart burst. I had also never been prouder of myself. While I may feel differently today on how things were managed and the choices I made, I look at this birth with pride. The secret ingredients for this birth were trusting in my provider, confidence in my body, and a partner with strong arms. Most importantly, I was introduced to two more great loves of my life, Mateo and birth.

Birth #2

The birth of my second was an experience I learned a great deal from. I had just begun to train as a doula and had only attended one birth while pregnant. I continued to work with the same OBGYN/Midwifery practice as I was comfortable with them and still adored my midwife. This time around, however, I was going to get a doula. Not only did I desire her support, but I also wanted to take notes from an experienced doula before I started my own career. This was another choice I will always be grateful I made. My husband and I took a half-hour drive to meet Vanessa Lewis in a coffee shop. She was professional, which was impressive, but more so, she exuded knowledge on everything birth and had an endearing calm about her. We walked out of the door to that cafe and knew she was the one for us. No other interviews were required.

Our little one was due on New Year's Day. I knew it could be any day the baby decided it was time, but the one day I did not want my baby to be born was Christmas. I wanted that particular Christmas for my first born, Mateo, to be spoiled and showered with gifts before he had to share us with his soon to arrive little sibling. We again wanted the gender to be a surprise. Of course, my water broke on Christmas eve night while I lay in bed. I was surprised but held it together. I called my doula in the morning to give her the update. With her support, I found calm in staying home. She explained what would happen if I called into the hospital, as well as what ways I could make sure I was safe to wait for labor. Unfortunately, but fortunately, labor did not begin right away. I credit her with the birth, as well as the beautiful day I ended up with. Had I not had her information and support, I would have missed the unforgettable Christmas morning in which the father of my now three children proposed. My mother and stepfather, or as I lovingly call him, my Chuck, were there and were not only able to have Christmas with us but witness the proposal. For the record, I said yes!

I will admit my Chuck wasn't as comfortable as I was as I calmly went through the day, knowing my waters had broken. He definitely looked at me sideways a few times, and I watched amusingly as he gathered everything inside himself to keep his cool. As the day continued, I again became a bit worried about how long it had been and the chance of infection. My doula, who was also an apprentice midwife, simply said, "if you are uncomfortable with staying home then you should go into the hospital. I am giving you the information for you to make your own decisions, not to persuade you one way is better than another." She also explained how this would be managed when I went to the hospital. What an empowering conversation. The assurance I was in control of this birth and was the one making the decisions. I proceeded to go through my checklist to make sure I felt safe, including taking my temperature, feeling the baby's movements, checking for any cord prolapse, and drinking lots of water. I also used the acronym (T)ime (A)mount (C)olor and (O)dor for evaluating any risk. Ultimately, I was comfortable at home and felt safe, so I waited and waited and waited. The next day came, and still, no labor had begun. The anxiety of infection was getting to me.

I called into the hospital and was happy to hear my midwife was on-call. When I called at 9am, she giggled a bit at my hesitancy to come in and said I could take my time, but it should be within the next two hours at most. I dragged my feet. I arrived four hours later, at 1pm. I fibbed about the time my water had actually broken to give myself time at the hospital before they began Pitocin and thank goodness I had. When I was checked, I was a shocking 5-6cm with no labor, that I felt at least. I agreed to allow my midwife's recommendation to break the last forebag of waters[2], which seemed to still be intact, to see if removing that cushion would do the trick. Unfortunately, my stubborn body and baby, and boy did he turn out to be a stubborn little dude, still didn't get the hint. Pitocin was becoming more inevitable. With the suggestion of my doula, I asked to use a breast pump to encourage my natural oxytocin to move through me. The protocol was twenty minutes on and twenty minutes off, and the hospital supplied the breast pump. The first two rounds didn't make a change, but after the third and a little walk to the cafeteria, my sensations came on strong and grew stronger still quickly. I had my husband call Vanessa into the hospital. She arrived a little while later. She softly and quietly entered the space and applied pressure to my back while giving my husband instructions as well. I announced I had to go to the bathroom, and when I suddenly felt pressure as I was trying to relieve myself, my midwife said, "don't have your baby in the toilet!" There was a bit of laughter in the room as I was maneuvered to the bed on my back. I honestly didn't much care about my positioning, despite everything I knew about gravity or possible increase in tearing. Everything was happening too quickly for me to think clearly. At 5:27pm, I pushed my son, Davin Walker, out in three pushes. He was 8lbs 11 oz, and I had no tearing. My engagement ring glittered in every baby picture of me holding him that day. The secret ingredients this time around were expert support, knowledge, and confidence.

Birth #3

When I became pregnant with my daughter, I had been a doula for about three years. I had witnessed over a hundred births, and I had learned from the families I worked with. I learned what made a difference to each individual when they processed their experience. It was even more apparent to me there was no right way to give birth and how easily labor can take different shapes and forms. With the experience I acquired, knowledge of what my options were, and dream of what I always wanted, I knew home birth was for me. This time around, I wanted to be in my own home. I wanted to stay with my children, I wanted to avoid a hospital room and car ride, and I wanted to avoid unnecessary management or protocols. Regardless of how quickly my birth went, I knew the hospital was a hospital, and I knew in my heart I was ready to take this pregnancy, labor, and birth journey in a different direction.

I began the pregnancy going to the same obstetrics practice as I had with my last two children. Working as a doula with this practice had actually only solidified my positive feelings towards my past midwife, who still worked there with a midwifery team that had changed over the years. They were on the progressive side of care, open to discussion, and facilitated informed decision making and evidence-based

care. I also felt respected by them and therefore trusted them. All
vital aspects in finding a care provider. I was of advanced maternal
age (AMA)[3] at 39, and my midwife told me all about the protocols
and extra care that was standard of their practice, and I knew, probably all hospital-based practices. She also told me she understood
why I might feel extra visits, ultrasounds, and non-stress tests every
week in the last month of pregnancy would be difficult and maybe
invasive for me. She wanted me to know right away she was open to
discussing taking those out of the equation if everything looked good.
I was comfortable with this but also felt uneasy for a reason I had not
yet quite pinpointed. She was open, honest and said everything right
about how things were managed. What rubbed me the wrong way? I
believe now it was simply because the conversation happened in the
first place. Realizing extra management, regardless of what hospital
or practice I went to, made me question if I could have full confidence in myself and my body if I felt like all those caring for me did
not. I looked through the **Evidenced Based Birth** article on
AMA, and I understood why my pregnancy at 39 was managed in
the way it was, but I also decided I would like something different for
myself.

I called my past doula, now friend and Direct Entry Midwife
(DEM), Vanessa Lewis, and asked her if she would be my Midwife
this time around instead of doula. She was working with Michelle
L'Esperance and Joyce Kimball, who I admired and adored as well-
known and respected home birth midwives in Massachusetts. When
she accepted working with me, I was ecstatic. The expense of having
a home birth was always something that had me holding back in the
past, but this time around, we decided to make it work by making
continual small payments. We also knew it was worth whatever
penny we could scrounge up. The process was incredible. Having the
midwives come to my home for prenatal care was lovely. My two sons
and my husband could be part of the process. Additionally, towards
the due date, my sister, Brenda, who I had recruited as a photogra-

pher, was also able to come and talk with the midwives and myself about what I envisioned. It was a true family affair. We rented a birth pool from Vanessa, and Miguel and Brenda quickly got to work practicing with blowing it up and filling it with water. I mostly met with Joyce and Vanessa because they were closer in distance. Along with their check-ups, they would talk to me about nutrition and energy. They helped me to recognize my fatigue and low energy was because of low iron. After beginning a supplement, they recommended, I was a new person. My age of 39 was never brought up. At one point, I had a smaller than average fundus measurement which signaled an extra ultrasound. I had been told it was likely positional, and the ultrasound confirmed that to be true.

Three days after my due date on May 8, while I was shopping with my youngest son Davin, I started to feel a little something. I brushed it off, finished shopping, and went home where I had a friend and painter, Nuno, there finishing up our front entry room. I told my husband, Miguel, I was feeling a little something, but we decided it was ok for him to go to his dentist appointment that afternoon at 5pm. At 5:30pm, I called him to say, "you're going to want to get back here as things are picking up." He was able to come back home quickly and told Nuno I was getting ready to have a baby. Nuno gave me a wide-eyed "good luck and congratulations" and was out the door before I turned around. Miguel and I decided we should probably make the bed and put plastic on it while I called Vanessa. I was talking fine and had some time in-between the sensations. She told me to let her know if they picked up and she would be there soon. I also called Brenda and my mother, who lived two hours away, to let them know they could start making their way to me but not to rush. I still felt like I had some time.

In the midst of making the bed, I told Miguel I was going to take a shower. I noticed I was already starting to feel a bit of pressure when I went to the bathroom, so Miguel quickly called Vanessa back to let her know. She was then in contact with Joyce, who just happened to be in the car on her way back from a perinatal conference. I turned my music on and up in my bathroom and jumped in the shower. I might have been in the shower for twenty to thirty minutes when Joyce popped her head in the bathroom. I immediately started grunting. She ran downstairs to get her supplies. We laugh when we reminisce about Miguel frantically running around trying to blow up and fill the birth pool. He asked her how things were going with me, and she stated, "She's having a baby!" It wasn't long after that I was on all fours in my shower/bathtub, and Vanessa had arrived as well. My boys were playing in their room, and Miguel, Joyce, and Vanessa had all clustered together in my not so huge bathroom with me. At 8:24pm, I pushed my little girl, Sereia Leclerc, out on hands and knees in my tub into Vanessa's hands. According to Vanessa, Sereia had her hand on her face, which I felt! I pulled her through my legs and into my arms and had the biggest smile on my face, as did Miguel. My midwife somehow snagged a picture of that moment I will forever appreciate. My boys were ushered into the bathroom shortly after and gawked. My oldest son waved and said, "Hi." Little did he know he just met his best bud.

They stayed for a few hours after. My Mother and Brenda showed up a little while later, disappointed they missed all the action but amused it happened so much faster than I anticipated. I was so happy to have them there with me, though. After I moved to my bed from the shower, Sereia latched right away. The boys and my mother cuddled with me in my bed while we all swooned over Sereia. The midwives helped me to birth my placenta and finished up all their necessary inspections on my little girl. She was a healthy 6lbs 11oz. I slept beautifully that night, and my mother made me an amazing breakfast in the morning. While my labor and birth were my focus for having a home birth, it occurred to me right away the postpartum benefits of having a home birth were just as significant, if not more so. I never had to leave my house and put my baby in the car seat. I was able to sleep after birth and feel at ease with mine and my baby's care.

I was fed well and had support from not only family but birth professionals who were able to help me with breastfeeding. At one point, I had expressed to my midwives I was having quite a bit of soreness in my nipples. The midwives stated a small frenulum clip below her tongue looked like it would help. Joyce had experience doing this small procedure, and Sereia hardly made a peep. Any soreness in my breasts I had did miraculously improve. I spent my first two weeks snuggling my baby and spending time with my family. My secret ingredients this time around were family, environment, and trust in the process and my care team.

Conclusion

As a doula, I work mostly with families giving birth in the hospital. I fully recognize not everyone is a low-risk birth giver and with the means to be able to have a home birth. I also recognize babies and birth givers also have past medical conditions and give signs during pregnancy, and at the moment, more medical management is necessary and lifesaving. For this reason, I am extremely grateful for the experience and opportunity I had at home. I knew from experience I could manage labor without medicinal pain relief. I knew my body and baby showed no signs of extra concern. I knew, after supporting others at hospitals and from talking with my midwives, the procedures the home birth midwives took for my safety were enough. If anything did go amiss before, during, or after birth, I was still very safe. If my baby or I had shown signs and extra attention was needed, there was ample time to get medical attention in the hospital. I understand the need to feel safe in the hospital, but the word safe should be looked at more closely when speaking about birth. Does extra management in a hospital always equal safe when expectations and protocols for a mass of people are clearly not ideal for an individual? The answer is not black and white, and many people have successfully argued otherwise. What saddens me is when a low-risk individual wants everything a home birth offers but avoids it because of the perceived perception of safety. Always remember this is your birth. Home birth for the right person is safe, and a good home birth midwife will be open and honest about if it is safe for you.

The one aspect of home birth I'd like people to take away from my stories is home birth is home birth. If a birth giver is picturing an experience clearly pointing in the direction of a home birth, then home or maybe birth center should get the consideration it deserves. Hospitals are lifesaving and an essential part of the birth world, but acceptance of certain aspects between it and home is a must. Choosing a nurse midwife in a hospital is a smart choice for anyone low risk, but your birth will still be in a hospital with certain protocols. Every hospital uses consistent, maybe intermittent monitoring, even if evidence suggests it is unbeneficial. Every hospital will encourage you to have an IV, some are more open to omitting it than others, but it is always a conversation. In a hospital, cervical checks, done by providers and nurses, tend to occur more often and sometimes without informed consent, despite the mental barriers they may create, the trauma the procedure may leave behind, or lack of information it provides. A birth giver, their partner, or doula can bring decorations for the environment in a hospital room, but it will always be a hospital room. People supporting you within a hospital room are often strangers, though maybe wonderful strangers, still strangers. Once in a hospital, a birth giver is expected to have a baby. Your labor, birth, and brain are all combined, and labor takes on a life of its own based on what those three things communicate to each other. Time is relative. Patience, despite what any provider tells you, is something the hospital does not have the luxury of giving. You are there to have a baby, and providers want to do what they can to make that happen. This list goes on, so recognize the differences between home and hospital, which are impassable.

I was blessed with three empowering births I am proud of. Despite what I learned as a doula about what I could have done differently, I am proud of who was involved, the choices I made with the information I had, and how I felt in the end. In retrospect, I required a completely different set of secret ingredients for each one of my births based on who I was and what I believed to be true at that time. Every birth has its own unique story. The only way to know what will make a difference for your birth is by searching within yourself to decipher what is important to you, not to someone else, but to you. Sometimes labor and birth take on a life of their own, so find an environment and support you trust to take care of you in a way that works for you. Understand what your choices mean, how they will affect you and what could change. Do not put guilt or shame on one decision over another. Find confidence in the choices you do make and know labor and birth can be unpredictable and hard. Be proud of yourself no matter how your story unfolds.

---

1. Breaking of Waters – When the sacs, a two-layered membrane of amniotic fluid, surrounding the baby in the uterus break or leak.
2. Forebag of Water – The forebag of water is one of the two sacs surrounding baby that is exposed and bulges in the vaginal canal as labor and baby put pressure on the cervix and dilation occurs.
3. Advanced Maternal Age – When a birth giver is 35 or older at the time of giving birth

BETHANY A. LECLERC CD(DONA), CLC, APPAC

Bethany Leclerc was brought up in a small town in New Hampshire, but has found her roots growing in Hudson, MA, with her three children and husband. Her background in college was in modern dance, and after working as a dance teacher for a few years, she received her Master of Science in Arts Administration at Boston University. After her first child was born, her heart led her to birth doula work. In 2015 she became a certified DONA doula and began her doula business, A Golden Birth. Her passion for supporting birth givers pushed her to find other ways she could help perinatally. She took a training for Childbirth Education through CAPPA, became a certified Placenta Encapsulator through The Association of Placenta Preparation Arts (APPA), and became a Certified Lactation Counselor (CLC) through The Healthy Children Project, Inc. She now works with two partner doulas, and A Golden Birth offers a variety of services surrounding pregnancy labor, birth, and postpartum. She strives to continue to help everyone she works with know their own power, voice, and ability to give birth. Watching families grow and seeing their transition into parenthood has been an honor she is continually grateful to be a part of.

Website: www.agoldenbirth.com

Email: agoldenbirth@gmail.com

Facebook: www.facebook.com/agoldenbirth

Instagram: www.instagram.com/agoldenbirth

Links for those mentioned in your chapter

www.spinningbabies.com

www.evidencedbasedbirth.com

www.centerforbreastfeeding.org

www.thebirthhour.com

Vanessa Lewis, DEM and Joyce Kimball, CPM

TrinityMidwifery.care

NewLifeBlessings.com

Michelle L'Esperance, CPM

Warmwelcomebirth.com

14

PLANNING FOR SOMETHING AS UNPREDICTABLE AS BIRTH

KYLEIGH BANKS, THE AUTONOMY MOMMY

I CAN'T BEGIN to tell you about the journey to my home birth without sharing where it all started. Before getting into the details, I have to start by telling you that not only is my story not special — it's actually well within the realm of possibility for you. What story is that? The story of how I went from fearing birth so deeply that I didn't want children to having an amazing (and dare I say easy) unmedicated home birth by choice. Not only that, but I gave birth to my baby into my own hands, in my own bathtub, and the first words out of my mouth were, "I know you won't believe me, but that wasn't as hard as it looked."

Oh yeah, and she was nine and a half pounds, too.

What was my secret to having an unmedicated home birth that "wasn't as hard as it looked"? We'll get to that, but let's start at the very beginning when I was trying to conceive. Like most moms I know, I started listening to birth story podcasts before I was even pregnant. As I listened to the hundreds of birth stories on the most popular podcasts, there was something that wasn't sitting right in my heart. Nearly all of the stories I was hearing carried underlying themes of fear, pain and an incredible lack of control. On top of that, I heard mothers praising their OBGYNs for performing invasive procedures with no consent, for no reason, and with little to no evidence of benefit. For me, I knew there had to be a better way... and thus began my journey to finding the better way: home birth.

Throughout my life, long before my pregnancy, trust has been my default setting. I don't know exactly where the trait came from — maybe from laziness, honestly —but all I know is that doing nothing (except trusting my body) feels so incredibly normal to me. I don't seek out information to be convinced I need anything outside of myself, and I even have a tattoo that reads "turn to yourself" in Hebrew, meaning I am the one with all the answers I will ever need. So, when it came time to make the first big decision in pregnancy — Will I be having an intervention-free home birth or a medically managed hospital birth? — it was a no-brainer. Hospital birth wasn't my default, so I didn't need to be convinced that home birth was the better option. It was quite the opposite, actually; home birth was my standard. Trusting myself, my body, and birth was my standard, and not a single person could make a compelling argument as to why I should even consider giving birth in a hospital.

It's important to consider your biases about birth. How do you feel about birth at this exact moment? How do you feel about home birth? Do you think birth is an event that should be medically managed? Do you trust that birth can unfold perfectly if it's left undisturbed? Those biases and beliefs will influence all of your decisions, and your decisions will heavily influence the outcome of your birth. For instance, I personally believe that birth isn't a medical event to be managed or feared, but rather a transformational experience and a spiritual rite of passage; therefore, all of my choices ultimately reflect those beliefs. Obviously my core beliefs about birth led me to birth at home, but they also led me to do other out-of-the-box things like forgoing some prenatal testing including ultrasounds and other interventions such as cervical checks and membrane sweeps.

I want to note that I didn't decline any tests or interventions solely based on my bias that birth is sacred and natural. To make decisions that align with our core desires, I believe that it's necessary to foster critical thinking skills. In birth this is especially true because modern obstetrics tends to treat any variation from normal as a major complication or medical emergency. A good example of this is that you'll often hear what I would call an "unplanned cesarean" described as an "emergency cesarean." An emergency is a serious, unexpected, and often dangerous situation requiring immediate action, whereas most cesareans are performed after some trial and error and almost always after a discussion.

The first step toward critical thinking and decision-making in pregnancy and birth is simply understanding the situation enough to realize why you need to make a decision in the first place. Did you catch that? During my own pregnancy, I often thought to myself, "Why do I even need to be making a decision?" Remember, trust is my default. So when my own pregnancy varied from the norm, like when I gained over ten pounds per month in my second trimester, I would ask myself, "Is this a normal variation, or a true complication needing an intervention?" If and when I decided to even entertain the idea of an intervention (anything from ultrasounds to hospital transfer), then I would work my way through a series of questions. What is my gut telling me to do? What are the benefits of the suggested intervention? How about the risks? Are there any alternatives? What happens if I decide to do nothing? Do I have to decide right now?

I want to be super clear about something; you do not need to be asking your care provider these questions (though you totally can). You should be turning to yourself with these questions. You are here to cultivate your personal autonomy[1], not to learn how to be a good patient to your care provider. This is your birth, your body, and your rite of passage. You call the shots.

Connecting with your intuition and living autonomously are crucial aspects of preparing for birth. Not only did cultivating my personal autonomy transform my birth, but it transformed my postpartum journey and every other aspect of my life. A great place to start when developing your personal autonomy is with developing your self-confidence. The more you practice swimming, the more confident you'll be in swimming. It's exactly the same concept when we talk about building the confidence to stand up for ourselves in pregnancy and birth. The more practice you have in making autonomous decisions, the more your confidence will grow, and the easier it'll be to make choices that reflect your honest desires, free from outside pressure.

I want to make it known that when I say "I trust myself" and "I trust my body" it includes trusting my intuition. If my intuition had told me to seek further medical support at any point in my pregnancy, I would have done so without shame or second guessing myself. People often assume that in order to trust our bodies and trust birth in general, we have to turn away from medicalized birth all together. Instead of seeing women turn away from medicalized birth as a whole, I would rather see them tune into their intuition, and give birth where they feel most safe.

Often, standing up for ourselves doesn't come naturally. It's not unusual for someone to go through life constantly being told to "quiet down," to "respect elders," and to "fit in with the crowd." If you have never been someone who stands up for what you want, imagine how hard it will be to stand up for yourself during your most vulnerable moment of all — the birth of your baby. It's clear to me that cultivating self-confidence is something that every woman should be practicing in her pregnancy. How did I build upon my confidence to make sure I went into my home birth with zero self-doubt? I became hyper-honest with myself and with others. When someone asked me a question about my upcoming home birth, I answered it authentically without censoring it into a PG version or dulling down the response for their approval. I'm not going to lie, it wasn't easy, and sometimes it was actually pretty scary to be so subjected to other people's opinions, especially their opinions about my home birth. If for some reason I felt like I couldn't speak my truth, then I turned inward to examine why that was. More often than not, it was because I wanted to guard myself from the opinion of others... but in reality, I didn't need to be afraid at all. If you live your life authentically and unapologetically, then there is nothing to hide or be ashamed of. When I developed a strong sense of autonomy and confidence, other people's opinions no longer affected nor offended me. Other people's opinions told me much more about their own insecurities than of my own.

Another way I built my confidence in pregnancy was by killing my imposter syndrome. All of that doubt that you feel? Throw it out the window because it's not invited to your birth. When you're feeling like a fraud, or like you're not as strong as those other women who've had home births, I want you to remember this: your journey is unique to you. Your body and mind are just as capable as anyone else's. It's time to let go of everyone else's birth story and to make room for your own experience, whatever that may be.

Part of making room for your own birth experience to unfold is owning your actions for better or worse. It's called radical responsibility, and is something that every home birthing mother will come to know intimately. I knew from the minute I saw my positive pregnancy test that I would take full responsibility for my pregnancy, my body, and my baby. There would be no blaming outcomes on others, and I would never willingly give away my power of choice. This included erasing the words "I had to" from my vocabulary. Have you ever heard a friend say "I had to..." when they tell their birth story? "I had to get an ultrasound. I had to be induced. I had to lay on my back. I had to have a cesarean." Do you want to know what happens when we use words like that? We bottle up all of our innate power, and we give it away. I chose not to do that. In pregnancy, I chose to acknowledge that every single intervention was my choice and my choice only. I never had to do anything. I always chose to. I knew that even if my birth ended in a cesarean, it would be my choice and of course the best choice in the moment. Taking ownership of our choices and our actions and reclaiming our power over our births is a fundamental element to birthing autonomously. With radical responsibility comes the greatest prize of all: an authentic life. Give it a little bit of effort, day after day, and you'll be able to hear your intuition loud and clear and allow your authentic self to bloom.

The most profoundly true statement that I've ever heard about birth is this: you birth how you live. I heard it in pregnancy and assumed it to be true, and now after giving birth with zero medication and zero freak-outs, I know it to be true. If I could just learn to live calmly in pregnancy, I was sure I could bring that calm energy into my birthing space with me. I knew that it would take intentional practice to calm my mind, and that's exactly what I did. My intentional practice looked like this: connecting to all five of my senses while also paying attention to my breath. That's it. That's meditation, and that's the secret to fully embracing the present moment. To a total beginner, this is sure to sound like crazy talk, but if you can master this, then birth will be 'just another day' for you. Of course, it will be the best day of your life, but the pain and intensity won't be anything to run from or be overwhelmed by.

As you're approaching your home birth, it's not unusual that your thoughts can get a little out of control. Fears might be consuming you, or maybe you're constantly pre-living the future by playing through the worst-case scenarios in your head. Calming your mind is one of the more important ways to prepare leading up to your birth. The meditation that I encourage every soon-to-be mom to master is called the body-scan meditation, and it is fast-track to relaxing your entire body (including your mind) from head to toe. I start by closing my eyes and noticing any and all sensations in my body; this could be tingling, pulsing, tightness, soreness, itching, maybe even nausea or pain. As I continue through the meditation, I start paying attention to each and every part of my body separately, starting with my eyelids and gradually working my way down to my toes. After bringing awareness to each individual body part, I consciously relax that specific area, and when I sense that it's completely relaxed, only then do I move on to the next body part. When I do a body-scan meditation, I imagine that there is a continuous flow of relaxation running through me. By the time I have progressed from my eyelids to my toes, my entire body is tingling and warm. With intentional practice, you'll get so good at this calming technique that you'll be able to release all of the tension throughout your entire body, and you'll experience a monumental shift in your relationship with discomfort. You'll begin to notice that you can stay in tune with your body for longer, even if you're not particularly enjoying the sensations you're feeling, and this is exactly why the body scan meditation is the perfect practice for your birth.

Whenever I needed a dose of calm during my pregnancy, I did a body scan meditation to connect to my body. I continued that awareness as I added the awareness of what I saw and heard, and finally added in the awareness of my breath. Every single task I did throughout the day was a tool for me to practice living mindfully. Brushing my teeth, brushing my hair, eating, chatting with friends, all of it could be done with more attention and intention. What I was striving for was the exact opposite of "going through the motions." I tuned into my senses, noticed my thoughts, my emotions, my body as a whole. And noticed my breath. If you bring mindfulness to the forefront of every task of every day, you'll be more prepared for birth than you ever thought possible.

Did you read that last sentence? You are about to be more prepared for birth than you ever thought possible!! It really is that easy, and I know it because I've done it myself.

Practicing mindfulness and releasing birth fears go hand in hand. When I started learning more about birth, both hospital and home birth, I entered an intense dive into the literature. I spent night after night reading about anatomy, pregnancy, mindfulness, and fear, and then it hit me: an overwhelmingly clear message that forever changed my life. When we are faced with something we've never been through before, especially something as monumental and transformative as home birth, our thoughts tend to be motivated by fear. What if it hurts? What if I tear? What if there's an emergency? What if I die? What if my baby dies? But there's a catch; fear hijacks our ability to connect with our hearts and our intentions, which then causes us to make choices that don't align with our core beliefs.

I knew that in order to have the home birth of my wildest dreams, one with no fear, no second- guessing, no freak-outs, I first had to learn how to let go of the fears holding me back. The fears I once had of childbirth were never my own fears, and this became very clear to me after putting in the effort to understand the anatomy of birth. Most home birth moms share the same fears: "I'm scared there will be an emergency" and "I'm scared that I will have to transfer." In doing the work to overcome my own fears, I first had to get super specific about what they were. I knew that it would be harder to overcome vague fears, and being scared of "an emergency" wasn't going to cut it, for me. Was I really scared of an emergency or transferring to the hospital? Or was I actually scared of losing control? I analyzed my fears, asked myself hard questions like, "Wait, why am I actually scared of this thing?" and I realized that a lot of the fears I originally had were unfounded. Hollywood's exaggerations, as well as horror stories from friends who were dragged through the cascade of interventions[2], played a huge role in developing those fears. But they weren't my own fears, and after doing some more digging, it became quite obvious to me that I only had one real fear. I was afraid that the intensity and pain of birth would scare me. How ironic to fear fear itself, right?

I ended up giving birth with quite literally zero fears and, honestly, nearly zero emotions altogether. I removed my mind and ego from the equation, and I trusted my body to be in control. Our minds can get in the way of our births, and I often hear stories in which that's the case. So, what did I do to ditch my last fear, the fear of being afraid? To put it simply, I asked myself what was so scary about being afraid. I realized and completely embodied the fact that I am the one in control of my perception — no one else. I define my own reality. I knew that even if I became scared during my labor, I had the ability to watch the emotion without judging it. It takes a spiritually open-minded person to understand that there is a separation between "me" and "the feelings that I'm feeling." There can be fear, and you can remain unafraid, just as there can be pain, and you can remain unharmed. This concept is one that resonated so deeply with me that it actually turned into two of my favorite birth mantras of all time, "There is fear, but I am not afraid" and "There is pain, but I am not hurting."

Speaking of pain, have you ever heard the term "painless birth"? One of the most fascinating parts of my birth story is that I never felt pain in my vagina or perineum. Not once, and I promise I'm not exaggerating even a little bit. There was no pain in crowning, and there was no ring-of-fire, and honestly, I didn't even know when my baby was crowning or when her head came out, because it all felt the same to me: pain-free. (I credit this to the pain coping sessions I did in my pregnancy and learning how to release tension, specifically when feeling a burning sensation). No, I didn't have one of the mystical painless births that I've read about in books and online beforehand; I definitely felt pain as my cervix was opening. But the fact that I didn't feel pain as my birth canal stretched and even tore tells me that a painless birth is well within the realm of possibility. If you're reading this and shaking your head in disbelief, or even mumbling "bogus" under your breath, please just hear me out first.

Have you ever been in the shower and turned the water all the way to cold? If you have, I'm sure you know the feeling where your body completely tenses up and your mind starts to race. Some might describe it as painful, and almost everyone would describe it as uncomfortable. But it doesn't have to be! The more you practice this cold shower technique, the more you begin to have no reaction to the cold water at all. The physical experience is the same, but the tension and the discomfort that causes the tension diminishes. It is the exact same with birth. When I describe the fact that there was never pain in my vagina, I'm in no way saying that I didn't feel anything in my vagina. A painless birth doesn't mean that you don't feel anything. It means that the sensation you're feeling isn't causing you tension. You feel the feeling, and that's that. No big deal — you're not trying to escape the feeling or wishing it away at all.

Here's another example: have you ever known someone who's completely terrified of roller coasters, and another person who absolutely loves even the craziest of rides? Think about it. The only thing that makes these two people's experiences different is their own perception of what is going on. They experience the exact same event in wildly different ways. Does that remind you a little bit of how people describe birth? One person says birth felt like they were being torn in two, and then there's me, seconds after birth saying, "Wow, that wasn't bad at all!". What I'm telling you is that being able to release tension, and ultimately pain, is something that you can learn before you give birth.

I implemented something else in my pregnancy, something that almost nobody talks about but can make or break your birthing experience; I transformed how I dealt with discomforts day-to-day in my normal life. It made sense to me that if I were overreacting to discomforts in pregnancy, like Braxton Hicks or even stubbing my toe, I would bring that overreacting nature into my birth. I realized that I'm not going to all of a sudden be able to handle extreme intensity or prolonged discomfort without practicing first. So, whenever I stubbed

my toe, had lightning-like pain in my pelvis, or searing round liga-
ment pain in my side, I asked myself, "Am I overreacting?" Do yourself a favor and try asking yourself this next time you're in pain.
Watch what happens when you face your discomfit head- on, and
then consciously choose to let go of your reaction, your tension.
Watch how quickly the pain fades away. It's almost unbelievable. As I
started to embody the characteristics that I had hoped to call upon in
birth: ease, a calm mind, going with the flow, in reality, I was practicing and preparing myself for labor in the best way imaginable.

Perfecting pain coping skills doesn't come easy for most moms, and I
can't skip over the fact that I did several intentional pain coping practice sessions the last few weeks of my pregnancy. I sat with a bowl of
ice and would hold the ice intermittently for a minute and work my
way through several pain coping techniques. The techniques were
mostly ones I could do by myself and using nothing other than my
mind and body; breathing, meditations, reciting mantras, dancing,
singing, smiling. I would use one specific pain coping technique for
an entire minute and then actually write down how well the technique worked for me on a scale of one to five. As I got closer to my
due date, there were a handful of techniques that I knew worked, and
I had prepared to call upon them when labor became uncomfortably
intense.

Because I was planning a home birth, but I didn't have any friends in
my circle who had had a home birth themselves, I knew I had to be
proactive in finding other moms who have walked the path before
me. I found myself a tribe, through social media platforms and
podcasts, and I surrounded myself with stories of women who had
given birth at home with no interventions. Stories of unassisted and
completely undisturbed births quickly became my favorites.
Honestly, every pregnant mom (yes, even the one planning to have an
epidural) should surround herself with unassisted birth stories
because there is something so inherently powerful about a mother
trusting herself enough to bring her baby into this world completely

undisturbed. I often fantasize about what my future pregnancies might look like if I could be as trusting as those women with their wild pregnancies and their freebirth[3] stories.

For this birth, my birth team consisted of my partner, my mother, a midwife, and my sister, who's a photographer. It's incredibly important to put together a support team that knows, understands, and respects your desires and boundaries. My entire team knew that my desires came first (before my partner's, my mother's, and even my midwife's). Not only was it okay to acknowledge that fact, but it laid the foundation for me to show up in my birth autonomously. If you find yourself in a situation where someone from your birth team doesn't support you as the ultimate authority of your own birth, take notice and consider the implications of that. At the end of the day, you need to be able to live with the choices that you make for yourself and your baby. Also, remember that just because someone is family doesn't mean they need to be a part of your birth team. And to be brutally honest, sometimes they make the worst support people. I am not ashamed that I put multiple family members on "mute" leading up to my baby's birth. I also expected my partner to be the gatekeeper between his family and me so I could have some extra breathing room approaching birth. It was very important to me that the weeks leading up to my home birth were filled with a calmness and positivity.

With zero fears and my due date fast approaching, I found myself welcoming the unknown with open arms. I felt comfort in knowing that every single one of my female ancestors had walked this path before me. I spent my days bouncing on my birth ball while doing puzzles, patiently waiting for my baby to show me any sign that she was starting her journey down and out of me. My due date came and went, and one night, for no apparent reason, my emotions overflowed as streams of tears pouring out of me. I now know this to have been a clear sign that the birth process was starting. My hormones were dancing their most perfect dance, which left me crying on my bathroom floor as the energy cleared. It made room for the even bigger energy that was bound to come soon.

On February 9th, forty-one weeks and two days pregnant, and after an amazing night of sleep, I woke up at 7:00 AM and made my morning trip to the bathroom. I climbed back into bed, fell asleep, and soon woke up to notice that my underwear felt a bit wet. Sure enough, my water membranes had started to leak. My first text to the midwife was at 7:20 AM: "My water started leaking, there's a bit of meconium, and I'm feeling very light period-like cramping." As midwives do, she reminded me to get some more sleep, and that she'd be in touch throughout the day. A lot happened in the next ninety minutes. I took two showers, released all of my dark brown meconium water onto the floor of my bathroom, used a tens-unit, swayed and rocked, leaned on my birth ball, moaned, and moaned some more. At 8:50 AM, my partner sent his own text to the midwife, letting her know that "contractions are between two and three minutes apart." The midwife began to head in our direction. This was active labor.

The hardest contraction of the entire birth was one I had right before getting into the bathtub. Labor had come on so fast that I wasn't able to get control of my mind, and as tension started to build, I knew the bathtub was where I needed to be. I climbed into my oversized corner jacuzzi bathtub, which is where I would stay for the duration of my 9-hour labor. For the next three hours, I removed my mind and emotions from the equation, and I let my body open...

And girl, did it open!

I was in transition by the time my midwife arrived around noon. There were a handful of contractions that rocked me to my core, but never once did I even entertain the idea that I couldn't go on. In fact, when my midwife had said, "You can push if you feel like pushing," I thought that there was no way I could already be completely dilated. It's a great thing that transition came so fast because I would spend the next four hours both involuntary and actively pushing my daughter down and through me. The position I was in when I entered the bathtub was the position I stayed in for six hours. Looking back, I would bet on the fact that my labor would have been shorter by at least two hours if I had just stood up and let gravity work its magic. But during my labor, I felt safe on my back in my bathtub, lying calmly like I had done countless nights during my pregnancy, enjoying the water around me. After pushing on my back for two hours, I spent the next two hours moving between squatting and getting up on my hands and knees, still in the bathtub.

At 4:31 PM, my daughter was born, passing under the water, through my legs, and into my arms. Eyes wide open, she flailed her arms and looked right up at her father, whose hands reached out to greet her.

Nine hours. Zero fears, zero freak-outs, zero interruptions, and zero interventions. In just nine hours, I became aware of the immense depth of my strength, both body and mind.

Do you remember those birth story podcasts that I was listening to before I conceived? Not only did they lead me down a path of releasing each and every one of my birth fears, but they also inspired me to educate myself on all things birth and to reclaim my autonomy in pregnancy, birth, and ultimately in life.

How lucky I am to be here right now, passing that transformation onto you! You are reading this because you too know there is a better way to give birth. You understand that it's better to skip the invasive procedures done without consent, for no reason, and with little to no evidence of benefit.

You know that it's possible to rewrite the stories once riddled with fear, pain, and lack of control and emerge on the other side as trusting, confident, and capable beyond your wildest dreams. Remember how I never wanted to feel even a single contraction and how I almost wrote off having children because of my fear of pain? That frightened girl no longer exists. My transformation didn't happen overnight, and, as you can probably guess, your transformation won't happen overnight either. It won't happen this week and probably won't even happen this month. But over time, with clear intentions, consistent actions, and by building a phenomenal support system, it can.

Wherever your birth journey takes you, promise me this: that you will always remember that birth will never go as planned. As much as we can plan for birth, we will never be able to completely plan how it will unfold. Promise me that you'll remember that something will always be forgotten, and that, along the way, your desires will most certainly be adjusted if not completely changed. During my pregnancy, I was asked countless times, "Are you going to have a water birth?" I would always reply, "I don't know, I can't tell the future. I'll keep it as an option, but I'll always do what feels right in the moment." Never forget that you have the right to change your mind at any point in pregnancy, labor, or even mid-pushing. Give yourself the gift of trusting yourself so fully that you know you'll make the right choices in the moment, and then give yourself the even better gift of going with the flow.

In labor, and in life.

---

1. Autonomy- The quality or state of making decisions for yourself based on your knowledge, intuition, and desires, free from outside coercion.
2. Cascade of Interventions- The idea that using one intervention can lead to the need for more interventions.
3. Freebirth- A birth without the presence of a hired medical professional.

KYLEIGH BANKS

Kyleigh Banks, known as The Autonomy Mommy, helps soon-to-be moms overcome their fears, nail down their preferences, and create rock-solid support systems so they can have the births they've always dreamed of. She isn't ashamed to admit that she loves birth but hates the birth industry because of the degree to which interventions have become the norm — Kyleigh is more of a 'trust your body until proven wrong' type of gal. Through her free resources, digital courses, one-on- one coaching sessions, and doula support (southwest Florida), she helps both first-time and seasoned moms feel confident and relaxed, knowing that they're fully prepared for the intensity coming their way. By sharing stories on her podcast, Our Birth Wisdom, Kyleigh shows that even the most anxious first-time moms can ditch the fear and self-doubt and instead give birth however they choose (yes, even at home with no meds if that's their dream). Kyleigh's ultimate goal is to help moms release their fears, tune into their intuition, and make their births perfect representations of their desires. The result? A birth that a mom can look back on with a full heart, knowing it all unfolded perfectly.

Website: www.theautonomymommy.com
Email: kyleigh@theautonomymommy.com

Books: VBAC Queen, forward by Kyleigh Banks Podcast: Our Birth Wisdom

Facebook: www.facebook.com/theautonomymommy Instagram: @theautonomymommy

TikTok: @theautonomymommy

Clubhouse: @autonomymommy

Twitter: @autonomymommy

15

AN UNEXPECTED HOMEBIRTH

MOM OF TWO BOYS, DOULA, HEALTH COACH, LACTATION
COUNSELOR, PERINATAL MASSAGE THERAPIST, AND WRITER

MAIA WENTRUP

THE BIRTHS of my children changed me in different ways. During the birth of my first son, I changed into a mother. I learned what my heart and soul being connected to another human being felt like. During the birth of my second son, I realized the power and strength of which my body is capable when I surrender to her innate wisdom.

My younger son, PW, is a force of nature. He is incredibly active, can be impatient, and is often impulsive. He is also sensitive, caring, and intuitive. He is my 11/11/11 baby, and the way that he decided to barge into the world truly reflects his personality. He was going to wait for no one. He came quickly and with his arm up, ready to announce his arrival to the world. And it was completely, and stubbornly, all on his own schedule on that magical day.

Before Baby Number Two

The birth of my first baby, CJ, was a hospital birth. It was unmedicated and relatively quick, lasting only 8 hours from the start of my labor to his arrival. I labored mostly at home and arrived at the hospital two hours before he did. My husband, mother, doula, as well as a wonderful hospital midwife were there to support me and catch my baby. I never knew until the moment that I felt my baby coming down the birth canal that I could love a person that much. I felt a surge of adoration for this baby, unlike anything I had ever felt before. Of course, this was partially driven by the release of hormones meant to bond me to my child, but it was intense and amazing. A sensation that I will never forget. At that moment, who I was as a person was forever changed.

It was not only my life that would be different, but the way that I approached the world and interpreted the reality around me was on a different course from that of my pre-mama self. That woman that didn't want children at her wedding reception (yeah, I know...but I didn't know any better at the time) suddenly became utterly maternal, devoted to children and family, and incredibly well-versed in every "alternative parenting" book and research piece that I could get my hands on. CJ and I were best friends for the first three years of his life, with no one else there to shake it up. It was him and me together all of the time, and every move that I made was for that little guy.

Then there was the news...I had a second baby on the way.

Preparing for Baby Number Two

The big news that CJ would have a brother came as a bit of a surprise. It meant that everything was going to change, once again, in our family. I had settled into being a significantly attached mother to my first son, and the next ten months would be the lead-in to a completely different way of life. As I was preparing to be the mother of two, I worried so much about what the addition of another little soul would mean to my current relationship with CJ. To mitigate that anxiety, I planned. And I didn't do it halfway. I read. And then I did some more planning. And then I read some more. I got CJ excited about the idea of a little brother. I shared the news with the grandparents. I lined up the same doula that I had at my first birth, set up care for my son while I was going to be at the hospital, and made contingency plans for the care of our animals, should the need arise. I planned a hospital birth at the same local hospital, with the same practice, where I had delivered CJ. I was hoping for as wonderful an experience as I had the first time around. I thought that things were all in place for a seamless transition. Well, you know what they say, right? The best-laid plans, and all that...

Should Have Seen Trouble Coming

I first started to notice that things were significantly changing with the maternity practice and hospital that I had used for my first birth only a few months into my second pregnancy. When CJ was born, the maternity practice had been a mixed OBGYN and midwife practice that was unique, especially in a small community such as ours. While there may have been behind-the-scenes friction, I, as a patient, never saw it. It was unusual to find those two groups coexisting so successfully, and it always made me feel at ease that there was the midwife option, as that was where I found myself most at home. The way that it worked was that if a patient of the practice labored and delivered at the local hospital, they would deliver with the midwife that was on call on the floor. If there were complications or a patient specifically requested an OBGYN, then a doctor would be called. But in the majority of cases, each baby was caught by a midwife. This set-up offered an environment where the choice not to use interventions was not as unusual as in other nearby hospitals.

Unfortunately, earlier that year, our small local hospital had been absorbed by a larger corporate hospital system, and they were downsizing the medical care in our area. The financial bottom-line became much more important than patient care, and that reached across the board from Urgent Care to Maternity and beyond. Just as with any corporate take-over, there were lots of layoffs and changes with middle management, as well as facilities. But the change that affected me the most as a patient, at that time, was the attack on midwives that hit the Labor and Delivery floor and the maternity practice at which I was a patient. What had been a six to eight midwife practice when I had my first son, only three years earlier, was now being systematically dismantled. Midwives were being pushed out and shaved-off the payroll as doctors replaced their duties on the delivery floor. By the time I was approaching 36 weeks, there were only three midwives still working as a part of the maternity practice covering Labor and Delivery at the hospital. This meant a complete shift in practice culture and care. Not only were the midwives feeling overworked and disrespected, but there was more of a chance that a laboring mother would end up with a doctor when she wanted a midwife. The tension in the prenatal visits was also palpable. Instead of a welcoming feel, as I had experienced before, the halls were full of glares and whispers, and appointments included a discussion of whether or not there would still be any midwives available when I went into labor.

All these years later, I understand that changing practices would have probably been a good option to explore. However, at that point, I didn't know that it was something I could do. And this is a lesson that I happily share with women that I support now:

It is a mother's prerogative and right to change practices if she is feeling uncomfortable or bullied in any way. Starting maternity care with a practice does not obligate a mother to stay there, no matter what!

However, back then, besides acknowledging some anxiety about who would take my labor and delivery, I convinced myself that there was not much of a difference in my prenatal care. And the truth was that most mothers in group practices have their favorite provider or providers and feel anxiety about whether or not they will be the ones on call when the moment comes. I still saw the midwives that remained for my prenatal visits, and I tried to ignore my worries as the date for PW's arrival approached. But the warmth and care that I had once experienced as a patient there was gone. Appointments were cold, and the energy was negative. In hindsight, and as a professional doula myself, I see that my concerns were not unfounded. I did not advocate for myself because I assumed that this was the way that things were, and I was afraid to "rock the boat." I believed that I was powerless to change the circumstances of my prenatal care. I never want other women to feel as powerless or voiceless as I did then.

The Big Day Arrives

The early Friday morning that I went into labor with PW was the dawn of a cool November day. The night before, I had felt nauseated but assumed that it was due to eating too many carrot and celery sticks. I went to bed early, and CJ ended up sleeping in bed with us that night. The next morning, the sun wasn't quite up, and I woke to a "pop" and a flush of liquid as my water breaking snapped me wide awake. My son was still asleep next to me, and I picked him up and carried him into the living room where my husband was watching television.

"My water just broke," I said as I put CJ down to play.

My husband stared at me for a few seconds and then absurdly said, "but I have a work breakfast to get to."

"Well, I think that you're going to miss it. Call them and say you can't make it." I was starting to get a bit breathless now, and he realized that I was completely in earnest.

My labor was in full swing by then, and we both jumped into action. He called my mom to come and babysit and I got my older son ready for our departure. I also called the on-call maternity practice line to let them know that I was in labor. They passed along the standard message that they would inform the midwife on call, and she would call me back shortly. Fifteen minutes passed and nothing. My labor was progressing incredibly quickly, and I was starting to become uneasy, so I called back, even though they had told me to wait. Same response – they would have the midwife call me. They were sure that it had not been that long, and I should have plenty of time. I said that I would just head in, and they insisted that it was unnecessary, as "women often think that they are further along than they actually are." They would have someone call me. Still, no call came after another ten minutes, and I called back one final time. A different operator scoffed and urged that if I "really" thought I was that far along, I should come straight in because the midwife was expecting me. As a side note here, the midwives had never gotten my message. The one on-call left early since there were no mothers expected, and the new one stopped for a coffee since there was no urgency to get there. No one that should know I was in labor had any idea at that hospital.

Confused and having regular, forceful contractions, I was in the house alone with my nearly three-year-old son. As the contractions got more painful, at one point, I yelled out in pain, and my poor little guy said, "Mama, are you okay?"

"Yeah, Baby. Mama just wants us to sing." As I labored with my knees on the floor and my upper body on the couch, he and I sang. I do not remember the song. And I imagine that the singing was probably awful to hear. But what I do remember was that my reptilian brain screamed at me to protect both babies. The idea of scaring my son was loathsome to me, so I promised myself that I would be as quiet as possible so as not to scare him, no matter what happened. We continued to sing, and that one initial yell was the one and only one that I allowed myself in front of CJ. Years later, he tells me that he does not remember anything about that day except that he "played with" his grandmother.

Many things happened in the ninety minutes between when I was awoken and when my second son arrived. I cannot remember the exact order of things, and everyone that I have discussed it with, that was there, has a slightly different set of recollections. After all, it was nearly a decade ago. The peculiar truth is that I remember the sensations and feelings as if this all happened yesterday, but the specific details of the morning escape me.

As I waited for my mother to arrive to babysit, I still thought that I would make it to the hospital. My husband had spoken to my doula, and she would meet us there. We had a plan that I wanted to try to stick to. However, reality came crashing down when my mother arrived, and I got up to get ready to leave. As I bent down to put on my shoes, I believe I said something along the lines of "I am not going anywhere. I can feel the baby's head," as I sank to my knees near the front door.

An Unexpected Homebirth

My husband still happened to be on the phone with my doula, telling her that we were leaving, and she told him to hang up the phone, call 911, and get me into a comfortable position because he was likely going to be catching that baby. He began running around gathering what she told him to, and I simply rolled over onto the living room floor (luckily, I had vacuumed the day before) and allowed the waves of the contractions to wash over me while he gathered towels, blankets, gloves, and water.

From that moment on, things began happening around me, but I can only describe it all in terms of impressions, sensations, and emotions. People spoke in rushed whispers, EMTs appeared, and my doula came in. Later that day, I learned that the EMTs had just completed their training on delivering a baby, but none of them had ever seen it done in real life. As nervous as they were, I saw a lot of shaky hands and dropped jaws. My doula, who had decided to change course and come to our house, pushed one of the shaky-handed men aside as she slipped on gloves to catch the baby. My neighbor, who happened to be a NICU nurse, came over, and my husband waited alongside. There was movement of bodies and cool air from the open door, but I never even noticed feeling cold. I remained in my own headspace, with the exception of being hyperaware of where CJ was at every moment.

"I'm okay, Baby, go ahead and play," was my response the couple of times that he ran up to check on me. Other than that, I made as little noise as I could. I felt powerful in my body and completely unconcerned with anything but me and the health and safety of my two babies. And so, without screaming, without fear, and without hesitation, I delivered my second baby—pink and ready to take on the world with baby jazz hands (I was told that he had his hand up next to his cheek as he emerged).

When I share this story with people, I am very often met with "oh, that must have been so scary." I hear wonder that I delivered at home without medication. I hear disbelief that I was as quiet and calm as I described. (The truth is that my doula said that you could hear a pin drop in the room as he was born). And my response is always the same—a completely honest, firm, and reminiscent—"No, it was actually a magical, amazing, peaceful experience." I was in my home, where I feel safest. There were no bright lights, no medical sounds or smells. There was no question of interventions, so I was simply going through birth as a natural process, as opposed to a medical emergency. It was warm and comfortable. It was home.

I seriously considered just delivering the placenta and staying home once he was born. I felt so satisfied and secure with my nursing newborn resting skin-to-skin on my chest. My doula and my neighbor clamped the cord, and my husband clipped it. But I still did not feel that I had the resources that I needed and was not prepared for an actual home birth. There was no midwife, and I was not intending to have an unassisted birth. So I took the ambulance ride with my nursing newborn, heading to the hospital for two days of settling into motherhood with two babies.

And Then There Was the Hospital

Up until this point in the story, the only regret I have is that I did not feel in a position to remain at home now that the baby had arrived. I would have loved to settle into my own bed and happily and warmly nurse my baby between soft, familiar sheets. But it was not to be. I thought at the time that bringing him and me to the hospital was the best way to ensure that we would both be healthy and well-supported. But once that ambulance arrived at the hospital, the story twisted into one of many regrets that outweighed the blissful, happy memories from home.

When I arrived at the hospital, I was brought to a room so that I could deliver the placenta, which the EMTs had not allowed me to do in the ambulance due to a fear of hemorrhage. My baby was taken away to be weighed and cleaned without informed consent from me. A very grumpy doctor stomped into the room where I was to deliver the placenta, grunted as he sat, and started to go for my body without much of an explanation. When I requested a midwife, I was told that none were available, and he was who I was going to get. At that point, I still did not know that no one on the floor was ever informed that I would be coming in ahead of time. The lack of communication had led to a half-hour gap when the maternity floor was not covered by a midwife, and that was the time in which I arrived.

The doctor was on as an emergency back-up and had been sleeping. He was angry that he had been woken up and appreciated it even less as I was one of "those" women that "thought they could deliver at home" and "came to regret it." I tried to explain over and over that this was not a planned homebirth, which is why I was transported to the hospital, but he did not listen. And looking back, I really did not owe him any explanation.

It was such a relief to finally deliver the placenta, which had become incredibly uncomfortable to hold inside my body after so long. I also had a significant tear and would need to be stitched for a repair. The doctor was not gentle, and he had a nurse suction the area so he "could see," which ended up causing me notable physical damage. When I asked him to wait and give me a moment because it was hurting, he said he just needed to finish. When I asked if I could have some more numbing medicine, he said, "If you want to die, I can give you some more. Or you can hold still so I can finish this." By this point, the midwife had arrived, but she stood silent, just looking on with sympathy. With every pull, every stitch, and every dismissive word, I lost a little bit of the empowerment I gained delivering my baby safely at home.

The next two days held more and more negativity. I was stuck in an uncomfortable room at the back of an empty maternity floor and all but forgotten about. They had disposed of my placenta without my consent. I wanted to know the baby's blood type, which would require a blood test because they had disposed of the placenta. However, unbeknownst to me, when they took him, they tested him for drugs because it was hospital policy in the case of a precipitous birth. That fact was never made clear to me until some years later. That was never discussed with me. They also attempted to run a paternity test simply because I had asked for his blood type, which I did put a stop to. I saw lots of nurses rolling their eyes and even coming by to see the "lady who gave birth at home," as if I were some kind of a sideshow.

The nurses would speak loudly outside my room about how I was a "failed" homebirth. I hardly ever saw a nurse in my room, I never saw a lactation consultant, and they even failed to tell the photographer that I wanted my newborn pictures taken at the hospital. They said that they forgot I was there. These were just a few of the examples of the treatment that I was enduring as I attempted to bond with my new baby boy. When it came time to leave, I could not get out of there fast enough. I needed to reclaim the comfort and calm of home.

I ended up trying to deal with the pain from the repair within the same practice a few weeks later. They nonchalantly declared that they would schedule a surgery to re-cut the area and re-stitch it. I protested and said that I was nursing and did not want to risk exposing the baby to anesthesia if I didn't have to. The doctor rolled her eyes when I said I wanted to try a non-surgical fix first. I left, canceled the surgery when I got home, and promptly transferred my care to a different practice, at a different hospital. The physical trauma caused by the repair led to nearly a year and a half of pelvic physical therapy to fix what that doctor damaged. I also heard that the midwife that had left early was using my case as a reason to suggest parents not employ doulas because "some lady stayed home too long because her doula told her to." That broke my heart because she was the one that was supposed to be there. She was the one that left early, and I was left to pick up the pieces, while she betrayed my trust using me as a cautionary tale. Neither she, nor anyone else at that hospital, ever took any responsibility for any of the mistakes that were made that morning. In fact, they had the audacity to shift the blame to me and my doula, to whom I owe PW's earliest safety.

The Aftermath and Hindsight

If I could go back in time, as the person that I am now, I would have advocated passionately for myself and my baby, but at the time, I could not find that voice, and I allowed my power to be taken. I did not behave as the goddess that I believe all birthing mothers are. I was not honest with those offering me support and slogged through the anxiety and pain alone, not asking for the help that I needed. I cannot honestly say that if I could erase all of that heartache that I wouldn't do it in a heartbeat. All I can do now is to use what I went through to try and make something good out of it. At the time, I did not know it, but my path to becoming a doula and health coach for mothers began the day that I left the hospital. The seed for passionately supporting mothers was planted within me, waiting for me to work through my own pain and come out stronger on the other side.

For years now, I have worked to separate my memories of the hospital from my wonderful homebirth experience when I think of my birth story. It has been like trying to untangle a particularly difficult knot, with each thread leading to either the powerless feeling of being in that hospital, or the empowered, blissful memories of PW's birth. It has only been within the last year or so that I have been able to separate the two in my head fully. I no longer see my stay in the hospital as deserving a part in my birth story. It was something that I experienced and learned from, but I can now see the dividing line between PW's birth and our subsequent stay in the hospital. For so long, I felt pain when I thought of his birth, and now I can compartmentalize the day and feel that power and joy from being at home.

While I wish the experience had not been marred by my time at the hospital, I also cannot deny that each and every betrayal, abuse, and dismissal planted the seed of passion for change in me. I did not advocate well for myself in those days, and I was injured for some time, physically and emotionally. But after many years, it has led me down a path of supporting mothers professionally and truly believing in what I do. As a doula and health coach, I strive to support and empower women in pregnancy, birth, and motherhood. I want them to know their rights and learn to use their voices, as well as to be able to work through any birth trauma onto which they are holding. I want to help reclaim birth for women so that we may all feel empowered and capable as we enter motherhood. And I want to be a professional resource that women and families can turn to that does not judge or disempower. Women are forceful creatures, and I want to meet them where they are so that they can discover their own power for lasting change and strength.

I do not share my birth story with my clients most of the time. I do not want them to color their expectations or fears with my experiences. The fact is that I was blessed to have a safe, healthy, and quick birth, and the pain that came afterward had nothing to do with the actual birth experience.

I know that while my story may be unusual, there are hard-won lessons in it that I have carried with me, even until today, which may help another woman somewhere:

1. Birthing at home was the single most amazing, peaceful, and empowering experience of my life. Were I ever to have another child, I would plan a homebirth.

2. I realized eventually that I needed to learn how to advocate for myself and my child, even when the so-called "experts" did not see eye-to-eye with me.

3. Informed consent is not an option. It is a requirement.

4. No one should ever be allowed to steal your power. Information is power. Your voice is power. Support is power. Your instincts are power.

5. Not allowing fear to lead you into uncomfortable compliance is of paramount importance in birth and parenthood.

After All This Time

It is not unusual to carry our birth experiences into our lives as new parents. A calm and empowering birth has the potential to allow for an easier and more peaceful adjustment when our new baby comes home. A mother can enter into a new phase of parenthood without the burden of having to process the memories of a trauma. An empowered parent is one that can make decisions more easily and without the self-doubt that feelings of powerlessness can bring. I struggled for more than a year with pain and a lack of trust in myself after the experiences I had lived through during my hospital stay. But the one spark that pulled me out of it, as I processed it all, was the tranquility and pride I felt in my at-home birth.

It took me years to truly find empowerment in the memories of that day, but the way that it worked out affirmed for me the long-term value of a birth in which a mother surrenders to her inner power and knowledge. A homebirth experience allows for a quieter space where a mother can focus more on her body and her baby than on the noises around her. She is unburdened from the need to resist the intervention options flying at her while she is laboring. The interruptions are minimal, and she is the focus of her own thoughts.

When I picture a homebirth, I imagine warmth, strength, and maternal instinct. Even when I support mothers within a hospital setting, I find that I bring the lessons that I learned throughout all of these life experiences and professional knowledge into the room. I encourage them to tap into what they know and what they feel. Breathing some of the comfort and calm of a homebirth into any setting is one of my professional goals.

My emotions surrounding PW's birth are fierce and profoundly complicated, but I have come to believe that the opportunity to bring him into the world in my home spared me birth trauma that would have been nearly unshakeable had the doctor I dealt with that day been the one to deliver him. I am eternally grateful that my little force of nature knew what we needed. Power in parenthood comes from both the good and the bad, and PW's birth brought me so much of both to process. And as I touch the lives of other mothers and families in my work, I cannot ever forget where I was when all of this started, and where I am now.

Homebirth saved me that day, and the memories of it continue to save me all these years later. Meeting mothers where they are and supporting families in their own personal journeys feels like a privilege. Sharing my story is not easy for me, but when I see the dichotomy between me being empowered at home and robbed of my voice at the hospital, I know that the lessons I learned and share can have a wide impact no matter where a mother may be delivering her baby.

MAIA WENTRUP

Maia Wentrup is the mother of two adored boys, a Birth and Post-partum Doula, Lactation Counselor, Perinatal Massage Therapist, Health Coach, and Writer. She holds a Bachelor of Arts in Political Science and Spanish from Purdue University in West Lafayette, Indiana, and a Master of Science in Animals and Public Policy from the Center for Animals and Public Policy at Tufts University in Grafton, Massachusetts. She studied Muscular Therapy at the Muscular Therapy-Cortiva Institute in Watertown, Massachusetts, and Pre- and Perinatal Massage with Carole Osborne at Body Therapy Education. Her birth and postpartum doula training are through Birth Arts International. Her lactation counselor education is with Healthy Children Project, Inc., in East Sandwich, Mass-achusetts. And her Health Coach education is with the Dr. Sears Wellness Institute. She loves to learn and is always searching for ways to expand her knowledge. She loves spending time outside, hiking, running, and visiting the ocean. The lessons that she has learned in nature are some of her most profound.

Maia's passion lies in supporting mothers and families, as well as rescuing and caring for animals of all sorts. She strives, in her professional life, to empower mothers and families so that they can live their healthiest, most confident lives, knowing that they are making informed choices for their families. Her personal story and experiences have shown her that there is always a need for non-judgmental, unconditional support that meets people where they are. Allowing clients to be vulnerable while still offering help without shaming is something that she feels is often lacking in support services. She wants to fill that void for people, allowing them to trust their intuition and grow at their own pace.

Website: www.warmembraceperinatal.com
Email: warmembraceperinatal@comcast.net
Facebook: @warmembraceperinatalandfamilyhealth
Instagram: warmembraceperinatalandfamily
LinkedIn: maia-wentrup-16a10bb

16

ABOUT THE PUBLISHER

COLLEEN REAGAN NOON

COLLEEN REAGAN NOON is a best-selling author, educator and the founder of Wise Women Book Collective. Throughout her career, Colleen has held space for women and families: first, as an educator working with children, later supporting parents experiencing substance abuse and trauma recovery through her practice, The Respected Child. Today, she provides publishing services for women and continues to guide parents through several of her own titles, including the Amazon #1 bestseller *Baby Got VBAC: An Inspiring Collection of Wisdom for Better Births After a Cesarean.*

Through the Wise Women Book Collective, Colleen empowers women authors, aspiring authors and female-owned publishers to launch their books, providing them with resources, industry knowledge and individualized support. Colleen is respected for her expertise in both single-author titles and multi-author books, which are released under her own publishing name. To date, she has helped more than 35 individuals become best selling authors.

Colleen earned her B.A. at Rollins College in Winter Park, FL, and her Master's in Education at Lesley University in Cambridge, MA.

She is a mother of two and considers Florida, Massachusetts and
New York all home.

wisewomenbookcollective.teachable.com
www.wisewomenbookco.com

RESOURCES

Websites
- Evidence Based Birth https://evidencebasedbirth.com/
- Birthing Instincts with Dr. Stu http://www.birthinginstincts.com/birthing-instincts
- Birth Without Fear Blog: https://birthwithoutfearblog.com/blog/
- Spinning babies: www.spinningbabies.com
- Indie Birth https://indiebirth.org/
- POWERS https://www.pregnancyoptionswi.org/

Books
- Gentle Birth Choices by Barabara Harper
- Birthing from Within: An Extra-ordinary Guide to Childbirth Preparation by Pam England and Rob Horowitz
- The Birth Partner: Everything You Need to Know to Help a Woman Through Childbirth by Penny Simkin
- Ina May's Guide to Childbirth by Ina May Gaskin
- Natural Childbirth the Bradley Way by Susan McCutcheon
- Gentle Birth, Gentle Mothering: A Doctor's Guide to Natural

Childbirth and Gentle Early Parenting Choices by Dr. Sarah
Buckley
• The Natural Pregnancy Book: Your Complete Guide to a Safe,
Organic Pregnancy and Childbirth with Herbs, Nutrition and Other
Holistic Choices by Aviva Jill Romm
• Your Baby, Your Way: Taking Charge of Your Pregnancy, Child-
birth, and Parenting: Decisions for a Happier, Healthier Family by
Jennifer Margulis
• Fearless Pregnancy: Wisdom and Reassurance From a Doctor, a
Midwife and a Mom Paperback by Victoria Clayton, Stuart
Fischbein, Joyce Weckl
• Homebirth: Safe and Sacred by Kim Woodard Osterholzer
• Your Best Birth by Rikki Lake
• The First Forty Days: The Essential Art of Nourishing the New
Mother by Zheng Ou
• Immaculate Deception: A New Look at Women and Childbirth in
America by Suzanne Arms
• Give Birth Like a Feminist by Milli Hill
• Why Did No One Tell Me This?: The Doulas' (Honest) Guide for
Expectant Parents by Natalia Hailes and Ash Spivak
• Pushed: The Painful Truth About Childbirth and Modern Mater-
nity Care by Jennifer Block
• Like a Mother: A Feminist Journey Through the Science and
Culture of Pregnancy by Angela Garbes

Podcasts
• The Birth Hour
• Happy Homebirth
• Doing it at home
• Evidence Based Birth
• Dr Stu's Podcast
• Birthful
• Our Birth Wisdom

Documentaries
- The Business of Being Born
- Why Not Home?
- Happy Healthy Child: A Holistic Approach; Ultimate Childbirth Course
- Undisturbed Birth: The Science and the Wisdom (Dr. Buckley)
- Heads Up (Breech Birth)

Children's Books
- Hello Baby by Jenni Overend
- My New Baby illustrated by Rachel Fuller
- Our Water Baby by Amy Maclean and Jan Nesbitt

Made in the USA
Columbia, SC
13 July 2021